THE AVENGERS

DEADLINE

THE AVENGERS

DEADLINE

PATRICK MACNEE

TITAN BOOKS

LONDON

THE AVENGERS: DEADLINE
ISBN 1 85286 561 X

Published by
Titan Books Ltd
42-44 Dolben Street
London SE1 0UP

First Titan edition August 1994
10 9 8 7 6 5 4 3 2 1

British Library Cataloguing-in-Publication Data. A catalogue record
for this book is available from the British Library.

Printed and bound by Cox and Wyman Ltd, Reading, Berkshire.

CONTENTS

Chapter		Page
1	A Man with a Rosebud	9
2	Steed Joins the Staff	19
3	A Speech with a Difference!	26
4	Death on a Hot Night	37
5	A Part for Emma Peel	44
6	"Turning Over an Old Leaf"	51
7	Messing with "The Monstrous Regiment"!	62
8	Emma's Dutch Treat	78
9	The Stories that Never Were	87
10	A Killer in the Lift	96
11	What the Butler Said	111
12	The Printer's that was Dead but Wouldn't Lie Down	122
13	A Mystery by Wire!	131
14	A Turn for the Worse	143
15	The Night the Vans Left Early	157
16	Dilemma for Emma	166
17	"You Can Read All About It in the Morning!"	176
18	A Man Without a Rosebud	186

AUTHOR'S NOTE

I WOULD like to assure my friends in Fleet Street that THE COURIER and its staff bear no resemblance whatsoever to any real newspaper or newspapermen I have ever known.

Patrick Macnee gratefully acknowledges the help given to him by Peter Leslie in writing this book.

1

A MAN WITH A ROSEBUD

"I NEVER heard of anything so damned silly in all my life," the pink-faced man in the hairnet exploded. "What d'you think about it, Jeffrey? Don't you think it's the most ridiculous thing you ever heard of, eh?"

The man in the white coat nodded a sleek head, twisting the cords a fraction tighter. "I'm sure there are plenty who'd agree with you, General," he said softly.

"There you are. No, but I mean it's really too blasted much," the pink-faced man grumbled. "They were round at the War House this morning, complaining. The War House! I ask you! I mean, what's it got to do with *us*?"

There was a girl on her knees in front of Sir Charles. He lay back with his face hidden, one flaccid hand dangling as the girl busied herself with instruments. "Oh, I don't know, Anstruther," he said to the General. "I suppose they got so fed up with the F.O. saying one thing one moment, and denying it the next, that they felt anything would be an improvement. France, Holland and Italy, was it? I thought so. *Ouch!*—All right, my dear. My fault. Shouldn't have moved me hand."

"Still, you must admit it's a pretty rum go"—the fat man's enunciation was less than perfect, since a youth in rubber gloves was applying an electric vibrator to his jowls and the rest of his head was encased in a perspex dome crackling with ultra-violet light—"You must try and see it from their point of view. I mean, who *are* the beggars to believe? The Foreign Secretary or the responsible newspapers?"

The fourth client lay sheeted and silent beyond a no-man's-land of stainless steel and leather and glass, his elegantly crossed ankles resting on the marble washbasin surround. Beside them, a yellow rosebud languished in a long-stemmed hock glass. Into the steam which spiralled through the scented air from the hot towels cloaking his head, the acolyte ministering to him now

9

leaned to murmur: "They are speaking of the unrest abroad over the Foreign Secretary's speech at Grantham last night, sir. Do you wish to comment?"

There was a subdued muttering from beneath the anonymous white shroud.

"The gentleman says, has the minister denied making the offending remarks?" the acolyte called across to the other three chairs.

The fat man snorted into his perspex dome. "Of course he denies it. I had our P.R. people draft the wording of the statement before we took coffee this morning."

"I should think so," Sir Charles added. "Still, the damage is done now. Yes, just a touch of varnish today, I think."

The replies were faithfully transmitted to the ears within the towelling, but further conversation was subsequently impossible as Jeffrey, with a word of apology to the salon in general, switched on the noisier of the driers to attend to General Anstruther's silver hair.

Later, when Sir Charles, the General and the fat man had all gone on their separate ways and the assistants were tidying up before going to lunch, the coverings hiding the occupant of the fourth chair were swept aside with a single, lithe movement, the black Chelsea boots swung to the floor, and the man himself rose gracefully to his feet. He was tall and almost slim. His face, square-ish and determined over the cleft chin, radiated a debonair good humour. And his suit, dark and impeccable as his hair, was cut with an equal distinction and flair for the original.

"I shall have to bring you another glass on Friday, Adrian," he said, as he drew the stem of the rosebud through the button-hole on his lapel. "There's a quarter of a case of *Annaberg Scheurebe* which demands the presence of this one in my flat, along with its five brothers."

"Very good, Mr Steed," the hairdresser murmured.

"The *Tröckenbëerenauslese*, of course."

"Of course, sir. A little fruity, if it's the fifty-nine . . ."

"Ah, but it isn't, Adrian! It isn't—it's the *sixty-four*: immature, precocious . . . but a prince among wines already, my boy!"

"Yes, sir."

"Now let's see . . . I'll probably be wearing Super Star by the weekend. Or Baccara. I wonder which glass . . ."

"A burgundy glass, Mr Steed?"

"No, no. Burgundy glasses for the *crimsons*, Adrian. Claret,
I think, for the scarlets and orange-reds. And, of course, hock
glasses for the whites and yellows."

"Very well, sir. I'll leave room on your shelf for a claret
glass."

"Splendid."

The man with the rosebud adjusted the curly brim of his
bowler in the looking glass just inside the door, stepped back
to consider the result, tilted it a hairsbreadth more towards the
right, and then sauntered through the scrolled doors of *Jeffrey:
Styling for The Hair since 1792* into the noonday heat of Jermyn
Street.

He bought a couple of ties in Mason's Yard, ordered some
shirts from a man in Duke Street whom he had not patronised
before, bought an evening paper, and finally lifted his rolled
umbrella to hail a cab in St James's Square.

The taxi-driver reached behind him to open the door with a
practised hand, without bothering to turn his head.

John Steed sank back on the cushions with a sigh of relief.
The pavements were dusty and the sun was beginning to melt
the tar on the road. He found shopping in the summer a trifle
exhausting. "Westminster Mews, please," he called as the cabbie
slid aside the glass partition. "Number Five—at the far end."

"Sorry, guv."

"I *beg* your pardon?"

"I said, Sorry, guv. No can do."

"May I ask why the deuce not?"

"Orders."

"What the devil—" Steed leaned forward with an alacrity
astonishing in one apparently so lethargic. "Oh—it's you,
Benson. I didn't recognise you at first. Why didn't you say so
when I got in?"

"Not after last month, Mr Steed. You might remember a
pressing appointment again and duck out. His Nibs wouldn't
like that. My orders are to get you to him, and that's that. Fine
morning for me, it's been, I can tell you—cruising about *this*
manor trying to keep the cab free! I could've used your brolly
to beat off the Yanks while you kept me waiting, getting yourself
all tarted up and that."

"My dear fellow, if I'd known . . ."

"That's all right, Mr S. Never you mind. You're to have lunch with His Nibs, by the way. At the club."

"Oh, God."

"You'll be having a fine old nosh in there all right," the driver remarked as he swung the cab left into Jermyn Street again. "Wine. A grapefruit cocktail with roast chicken after, I shouldn't wonder . . ."

Steed sighed again. "No," he said, "knowing the catering secretary, I shouldn't wonder."

A few minutes later, the taxi deposited him at the foot of the marble steps leading up to the Nash portico near Prunier's. "Go on, then: you get up them stairs and do yourself a bit of good," the taxi-driver said, reaching back to open the passenger door again. "Better make it look real—that'll be four-and-nine, sir, if you please."

"Here's four-and-ten, my good man," Steed said with a perfectly straight face. "You may keep the change—and if it wasn't so near St James's Palace, I'd make it more real still and have you salute!"

"Narky old so-and-so," the driver murmured affectionately as he watched the dandified back disappear through the swing doors.

On the first floor, Steed found a wing-back chair near the Adam fireplace in the smoking room. He sipped a pink gin and scanned the front page of his paper while he waited. BRITISH EMBASSY IN PARIS STONED screamed the five-column banner at the top. DUTCH OPPOSITION CALL FOR DIPLOMATIC BREAK WITH BRITAIN warned the six-line heading over the single column story beside it. And in the middle of the main story a prominently displayed panel reported: ROMAN RIOTS CONTINUE.

The text of the panel was set in bold face type.

From McGregor Trask, Rome, Tuesday (it began). Carabinieri joined militiamen and Roman police today in an attempt to protect British property in the Italian capital as the anti-British rioting, which had started in the early hours of this morning, swept to a new climax before lunch.

The ugly situation worsened when militiamen who had been guarding the British Embassy from a stone-throwing mob turned round and began to help the crowd by supplying them with missiles.

As I walked down Rome's Via Veneto this morning . . .

"Ah, Steed. Briefing yourself a bit before the meetin', eh?" The august voice was above and behind him. Steed jumped to his feet. "Good morning, sir. I'm sorry, I didn't see you come in . . ."

"No reason why you should have done. No reason why you should have done, what? Now. Splendid. Ah—I don't believe you know Lord Borridale?" He gestured vaguely towards the smoking room's only other occupant, a white-haired, thin-faced man with black eyebrows and an imperious blade of a nose. He was about five foot two. And he owned a quantity of newspapers and magazines.

"Delighted. Steed—John Steed," the man with the rose in his buttonhole supplied. His Nibs customarily forgot such trivialities.

A steward came in and distributed menus. "Well, let's decide and order," the august voice said. "Then we can get down to business. They tell me the chicken's very good . . ."

A little while later, at a round table in a corner of the sunny dining room, he gestured again at the paper Steed had left on an empty chair. "What about this, eh?" he said. "British Embassy in Paris stoned indeed. Whatever next!"

"I thought for a moment it meant that the Ambassador was drunk," Steed murmured.

"That's a point." Borridale removed a small notebook and pencil from an inner pocket. "Rotten headline. Holding the paper up to ridicule. Can be read two ways." He scribbled a few words on the page. "I'll see that the man responsible is fired."

"I'm sorry; I'm terribly sorry. I didn't mean . . ."

"No, no. Quite right. Glad you mentioned it. Now—can we get down to brass tacks, please?"

"Yes, of course. Now, Steed, you may know some or all of this. I shall assume you do not, so that I can fill you in on the complete story."

"Right, sir."

"Right. Now you've seen these stories in the papers—riots in Paris and Rome and Amsterdam. Anti-British riots, Steed! In the three of the most friendly countries . . . There have also been other things that haven't got into the papers yet: unfriendly speeches castigating this country in various national assemblies;

student demonstrations and window-smashing episodes in
cities that are traditionally *pro*-British; stiff little notes handed
to our Ambassadors, and so on. I say!—this Beaujolais's not
bad, is it?"

"It's very . . . agreeable, sir."

"Yes. Well, this is nothing to what the Foreign Office has had
to put up with here in London. Outraged foreign Ambassadors
have been calling to protest since eight o'clock this morning.
And as for the countries *not* friendly towards us . . ." He left
the sentence unfinished.

Borridale nodded soberly. "The intercontinental wires, as one
of my junior subs might say, are humming!"

"I don't mind telling you, Steed," His Nibs continued in a
low voice, "that even the Americans—in the friendliest possible
way, of course—have expressed concern." He leaned back to
observe the effect of his words. Steed stared blandly back,
politely waiting for him to continue.

"Now all this is due," he went on at length, "to the Foreign
Secretary's speech at Grantham last night. But Borridale here
knows more about the mechanics of the thing than I do. I'll let
him get on with it."

"It wasn't a major policy speech," the press baron said. "So
it wasn't covered by any of the continental news agencies. Nor
was it a speech expected to make headlines here—he was only
saying a few words to the local Association, after all—so there
was nothing for the London correspondents of foreign papers to
pick up from our papers and cable home. Yet it was a speech
that has managed to antagonise practically every friend in the
West we have—once they've read the British papers on sale in
their country.

"And the most regrettable thing of all, Steed, is that this isn't
the first, it isn't the second, but the *third* time such a thing has
happened in two months!"

His Nibs took a short, fat cigar from his pocket and clipped
off the end with a device he wore on his key chain. He drummed
his fingers for a moment on the tablecloth.

"There's just one other thing of importance about this speech
that I can tell you," he said. "The Foreign Secretary did not in
fact make it."

Steed whistled. "You mean an impostor went to Grantham?"

"No, no. Sir George was there all right. Just as he was at the other two places where inflammatory speeches were reported. And he made *a* speech at each of 'em, too. But he did *not* speak the actual words, reported in continental editions of British papers, which have caused all the fuss."

"What *did* he say, then?"

It was Borridale who replied this time. "Same thing in each case," he said curtly. "Innocuous stuff purely for local consumption. Re-hashes of domestic policy points slanted to keep the local party people happy. Hardly worth a line in the nationals here. Good stuff for the locals, though—and worth a par below the fold, inside, for the provincials."

"The speeches were reported in the dailies here?"

"Some of 'em carried a bit. Not a single one of the remarks which have stirred up our friends abroad were quoted, though. There's no doubt about it—and this is confirmed by witnesses on the spot—he didn't make 'em. Not one."

"But—that means, surely . . ." Steed hesitated . . . "that means the *continental* editions of British papers involved must have been tampered with?"

"That's about the strength of it."

"But how can that be?"

"That," said His Nibs, striking a vesta and setting fire to his cigar, "is precisely what I had Benson bring you here to discuss. *You're* going to find out . . ."

"Yes, sir."

"And I don't mind telling you, Steed, it's a devilish urgent job. H.M.G. are shaking in their shoes about it. Another couple of stories like the one today, and it could bring 'em down, you know. It could bring 'em down."

"But surely, sir—"

"Oh, it could you know," Borridale chimed in. "The P.M. was telling me this morning. Disastrous loss of prestige abroad, loss of faith in the value of our—what shall I say?—our integrity, our probity. And after that, of course, loss of faith in the pound. And that would be it . . ."

"I see. Presumably, though, the Foreign Secretary issues an official denial as soon as he knows the bogus story has appeared?"

"Oh, yes. At once. But what's the point? It's not much good, once the damage is done, saying 'It wasn't me!'—even if you can prove it wasn't. Makes you look a damned fool, too.

Almost as bad for prestige as the original fake story. Besides . . ."

"Yes, sir?"

There was a short silence.

"Do I understand"—Steed chose his words carefully—"Would I be right in thinking that there's a—history—of the Foreign Secretary having expressed, privately, views similar to those attributed to him in the bogus speech reports?"

There was another short silence. His Nibs tipped the ash from his cigar into a coffee saucer. "Well, now, that's the hell of it," he said morosely. "In fact there is."

"What sort of views are they?"

"Oh—you know. Abroad begins at Calais. All Spaniards are slackers. The French think of nothing but money and try to cheat everybody. The Italians eat garlic and run away in battles. We fought the war just to get Europe out of the mess it had got itself into, and they should still be jolly well grateful for it—the usual sort of nineteenth century jingoist claptrap one expects from people like old George," His Nibs said with a superb unconcern for irony.

"And is he known for having such views? Does he express them in private often?"

"Well, that's not to say often. He *has* them, and I dare say he airs them now and then. Mind you—he'd never *dream* of saying so in public: he's been in the Foreign Service ever since he left Oxford. But most people know that old George is a bit old-fashioned."

"So that those who know him well would be all the more ready to believe that he actually did make this speech?"

"I suppose so. No doubt that's why they doctored *his* speeches and not the P.M.'s or someone else's. Let me make it clear, though—he does not hold these views in any sense like a favourite hobbyhorse that he's always riding."

"Quite so, sir. Now may I just get this straight? Sir George Carew—who holds somewhat . . . er . . . chauvinistic views privately but never expresses them publicly—makes a minor speech to a local political association. The speech is circulated in advance by his P.R. office but it's not important enough to be covered in person by London correspondents of foreign papers, by foreign newsagencies, or even the major British dailies?"

"Right."

"It doesn't state any views of importance on foreign or domestic matters—and the few British papers that do report it only carry a few words giving the general outline?"

"That's it—basing their stories either on the advance text or else on the Press Association wire report filed by the man on the spot who took it all down in shorthand."

"But when these same British papers reach the Continent, they are carrying stories reporting quite a different speech—one that Sir George never made at all—which insults all our European allies?"

"That's it, Mr Steed."

"Mind if I ask a few questions?"

"Fire away."

"Do these fake reports appear in continental editions of all the British dailies?"

"No, only in three. The same three in each case."

"And were these three the only British nationals to report the genuine speech at home?"

"By no means. Several of the others carried short bits—which appeared unchanged in the continental editions."

"Then," Steed said, "there must obviously be a special reason why these three papers were doctored. Or a reason why it's *easier* to tamper with them. Which three are they, by the way?"

"Mine—the *Courier*, you know—and the *Gazette* and the *Globe*. But the *Courier* stories were altered far more than the others, which is why I'm particularly concerned to get to the bottom of the thing. I get enough accusations already, claiming that I slant the news, without bothering about this kind of thing!"

"How were the alterations done?"

"At the moment, I simply cannot imagine. It seems impossible."

"Anyway, Steed"—it was His Nibs breaking in, looking at a huge gold turnip watch he had fished up on the end of his chain—"I suggest you go down to the *Courier* building with Borridale and see what you can find out there. I must be off: I promised the old man faithfully that I'd be at Downing Street by three . . ."

The press lord was looking uncomfortable, shifting about in his chair. "What is it, Borridale?" the august voice asked kindly. "Come on, speak up!"

"Well, there is one thing. It's just that, as a newspaper proprietor, I'm for ever being accused of using my paper to try and influence the Civil Service, of messing in party politics or slanting the news to bring the Treasury into disrepute. Or something. So—nothing personal against Mr Steed here, who I'm sure is a most excellent fellow—I must make one thing clear. I don't want my newspapers *in any way* mixed up in anything resembling a departmental squabble . . . consulting one section when I should have gone through another; that sort of thing. I mean, perhaps one ought to have asked C to come over and—"

"Not a bit of it."

"It was just that I happened to know you . . ."

"My dear fellow. Let me explain our security set-up. Some ruddy columnist or other does it every week in your papers, so I don't see why I shouldn't give my version! To begin with, there's M.I.5. They work with the Special Branch to clear up spy rings here, keep an eye on likely defectors among chaps with classified information, generally act as counter-intelligence. Then there's M.I.6—they get information *for* us from abroad. What the general public likes to think of as 'the secret service'. And finally there are the descendants of Maurice Buckmaster's lot in the war—the old S.O.E. mob, who are in a sense distinguished amateurs."

"Yes. One was fairly familiar with the general outline."

"But beyond all these, Borridale, there remains a small and select band of men and women more off-beat than any of 'em. They are available for any kind of work, anywhere. They can overlap or circumvent all or any of the others. And they are personally responsible to me and to nobody else. Nobody."

"Not even their own department?"

"They couldn't be. There isn't a department."

"And Mr Steed is one of them?"

His Nibs nodded as he pushed back his chair and rose to his feet.

"Right. That's good enough for me. I'll be in touch—and thanks again, Mr Steed—you and I have business to discuss in E.C.4. I suggest we call the porter and ask for a cab . . ."

2

STEED JOINS THE STAFF

GREENING'S ROW twisted a tortuous path between Fleet Street and Fetter Lane. A hundred yards from the Fleet Street end, the post-war rectangle of Borridale Court led to the *Courier* building—a huge glass matchbox on its end, a modernistic tower dwarfing the thick-walled nineteenth century brick and stone clustered around it.

From a centrally placed ornamental fountain, white lines radiated to dragoon the cars of the privileged towards a half circle of neatly ticketed name boards on white posts. At one side of the building, the snout of an articulated lorry unloading gigantic rolls of newsprint projected from a covered passage.

"Leads through from Shoe Lane," Lord Borridale remarked, waving in the direction of the passage as he helped Steed from the taxi. "You'd better come up to my suite. We'll be more comfortable there."

They threaded their way through a group of men in overalls sitting smoking in the sun with their backs to the wall of the building. Several of them grinned at the press lord, and one or two ventured that special wink combined with a slight turn of the head which signifies among working men the world over the successful scaling of class barriers.

"Machine-room men and so on," Borridale said over his shoulder as they went in at the glass main doors. "Taking their tea break before the edition. Splendid chaps."

Inside the cool, green foyer, rubber composition tiles muted the footsteps of the multitude. Three pontifical men in black uniform listened, advised and consented or refused with equal impartiality at a large reception desk. The hands on the clock above their heads stood at twelve minutes past three. Lord Borridale, apparently under a compulsion both to explain and interpret all that they passed, nodded at the block of three lifts which faced the doors. "We'll take the left-hand one," he

19

said. "For some reason it's always the faster. That centre lift
takes an age."

"What about the one on the right?" Steed asked casually.
There was an *Out Of Order* notice hanging from the darkened
cage.

"Oh, *that*! Permanently out of order. God knows why!"

The lifts served sixteen floors, Steed noticed, the car they
were expecting being at 11. As they waited for the flashing
marker light to descend the indicator column above the gates,
he looked curiously around the ornate foyer. Several small groups
of dark-suited, professional-looking men stood about, deep in
conversation. Ill at ease, diffident or truculent according to their
natures, readers and members of the public sought information
at the desk or turned the pages of the free papers provided on
lecterns at the opposite side of the hall. There was a considerable
amount of coming and going by less formally dressed men
and women—presumably staff personnel, Steed thought—up
and down the wide marble stairs curling out of sight around
each side of the lift block.

"Second floor or below, they're supposed to walk," Borridale
said, answering Steed's thoughts for all the world like the Red
Queen in *Alice*. "That's the main editorial floor, the second."

At the foot of the nearer staircase, a young man rested one
foot on the lowest tread and argued amicably with a fashionably
dressed, thin woman of about forty with tired make-up. He was
thirtyish, with fair hair flopping forwards over horn-rimmed
spectacles and the sleeves of his white shirt rolled half way
up to his elbows. "Now look, dear," he was saying, "you know
I can't do that. We've got *These You Have Loathed* on the
centres tomorrow, and it just wouldn't go, now would it? Let
me put it on four, like I said."

The woman gave an exclamation of impatience. "I've *told*
you, Laurie," she complained, a cigarette wagging from her
mouth as she talked, "the Grey and Harpsley ad's on page four.
You can't—you simply can't—run a piece plugging a man's
product, and then carry an ad from his biggest competitor in
the next column; it's just not on."

The young man lifted the large sheet of layout paper he
was holding down at one side and inspected it. "Well, I don't
know, Marge," he sighed. "I wish you Features people'd just
look at the dummy occasionally before you sit down to type

out your deathless bloody prose, really I do. It can't go on the centres, that's for sure . . ."

But where it *could* go—or what it was, for that matter— Steed was never to know. The lift gates slid open with a hiss of compressed air and soon he was accelerating upwards through the core of the building towards the penthouse floor where Lord Borridale had his private suite.

It was more a *pied-à-terre*, really, than a flat: a shower room, a microscopic kitchen, an expensive cupboard to sleep in— and an enormous living room, all deep-pile carpet and low, natural hide armchairs, with a teak bar and a desk of truly heroic proportions at one end, and a complex hi-fi, television and radio layout at the other. "These look straight down to the street behind the building," Borridale said, indicating the wall-to-wall windows behind his desk. "But those over there lead to a terrace. Shall we sit out—there might be more air?"

Geraniums in stone urns, bay trees in tubs and a hedge of macrocarpa growing in wooden troughs lent the roof garden a specious air of terra firma. Steed sat down at a white wrought-iron table in the shade of a striped umbrella as the proprietor went in search of drink.

The metal chair was scorching. The sun beat fiercely on the gravelled asphalt of the roof, searing the crimson, scarlet and mauve flowers and shimmering the hot air rising from the balustrade. Beyond, the immensity of London wavered towards the west in layers of ochre and blue. "Pure Canaletto, of course," Steed observed as his host returned laden with a tray on which ice clinked sociably. Borridale shaded his eyes and looked at the view. Barred with shadow, the honey-coloured bluffs of stone receded street by street and square by square towards the distant silhouettes of trees etched on the wide blue horizon. "Yes," he said. "I see what you mean. Bit higher up, though, than the view from Richmond House, eh?"

He leaned over the balustrade for a moment, gazing at the antlike complexities of people and traffic below as though reassuring himself that his view was indeed superior to that in the eighteenth century masterpiece in the National Gallery. "There's the Hilton," he said. "No—half hidden by that church tower. And that's the Castrol Building. And there's the new one at the top of Charing Cross Road. And there's New Zealand House . . . Oh, yes—and that one right over there to the left, that's the Vickers building on the Embankment. I think I like that best: one gets a little tired of slab sides. Even if one does have them oneself . . ."

He sat down in a swing settee with a blue awning over it and looked across at Steed. "Well," he said. "What do you want to know?"

"How *you* think it was done, for a start."

"I told you. No idea. More profitable to ask me my opinion of how it *couldn't* have been done."

"All right. Take it as asked, sir."

"Well, the faking couldn't have been done over there, for a start."

"Why not?"

"Not enough time. The bundles come off the aircraft—wherever it is—and go straight to the wholesaler or retailer. Practically straight on to the street, in fact. They're never out of sight long enough."

"Does this apply just to your paper, or to all of them?"

"All of them."

"And what actually has to be done—to insert, as it were, a bogus story in a paper?"

"There are only two ways it can be done: either the false story is substituted for a genuine one somewhere along the line *before* the paper is printed; or the change is effected afterwards—which means whoever did it would have to strip off the outer fold from every copy (that is, the front page and page two, plus the back page and the one inside that), and have substitutes ready to put in their place. And this would require far more time—and space to do it in—than I can imagine being available."

"And if the substitution is made before printing?"

"It's up to you to find out how, Mr Steed. I've told you, I have no idea."

"You did say you had ideas how it *wasn't* done, though."

"True. And I mentioned one. Here's another: I do not for one moment believe that any substitution could be made at the editorial level without someone finding out. There are too many people involved."

"When you say the editorial level, Lord Borridale, do I—"

"My dear Mr Steed," the press lord interrupted, "do you know how a newspaper is produced? Technically and chronologically, I mean."

"Well, roughly speaking, yes. But the finer points . . ."

"I am sorry to interrupt you for the second time," the dynamic little man with the black eyebrows said, "but I fear you will have to listen to a short address on the subject. Unless you know, you'll never get within a mile of anything!"

"Splendid!" Steed said hollowly. "And then?"

"Then I think the time will have come for you to join my staff."

"I was wondering if that could be arranged."

"Easily. I'll ring for my Managing Editor now. I think you'd better be attached to the gossip column as a leg man—that will explain your lack of specialised journalistic knowledge, for you could believably have been hired because of your social contacts. And it'll give you plenty of mobility, so that your new colleagues'll not be surprised if you're away from your desk a lot."

"That would be splendid. Do you have to tell your Managing Editor who I am?"

"Oh, yes, Mr Steed, I think so—broadly at any rate. I never interfere in the running of my papers, and if I suddenly appoint somebody over his head who (you'll forgive me?) knows less than nothing about the business, he'll either think I've gone off my head or that I'm usurping his authority. I must tell him something at least of the reasons behind it. I may be the admiral, but he's the captain of this particular ship—no doubt you are familiar with the analogy?"

Steed nodded and picked up his drink to accompany him on a tour of the geraniums as Lord Borridale went inside again to telephone.

A few moments later he was back, fanning his pink face with a copy of the *Courier*. "It'll be more convenient if we go down there," he said. "If you don't mind, we'll drop by his office in a few minutes."

"I should be most interested," Steed said. "In the meantime, you did mention a lecture on newspaper production!"

Borridale twitched his black eyebrows down over the bridge of his nose in a mock-scowl. "Did I sound that pompous?" he sighed. "Sorry. It's just that people always ask one *how* the business works. And it really is terribly difficult to explain a complicated, wholly professional operation in simple, nonprofessional terms. Very difficult indeed. However . . ." He paused a moment and then went on: "Take any paper. The day before publication, the advertising department advises the editorial department what spaces on what pages it has disposed of. At its simplest, the editorial then decides what material it will use to fill the remaining parts of those pages—and how it will be arranged and displayed and illustrated.

"The material itself will derive from a number of sources: reports from the various news agencies to whose teleprinter services we subscribe, news stories from our own reporters here and in the provinces, regular columns and other features from staff writers, cables from our correspondents abroad, and so on.

"In effect—and I must emphasise that this is a tremendous over-simplification—the editorial people then instruct the print-shop to carry out these decisions. Each story is set on a linotype machine, the relevant headlines are cast, the photographic blocks are made—and a compositor assembles each page according to the layout supplied. This is then proofed and, after the proofs have been suitably amended or passed as fit to print, the corrected page passes on to another department."

"Still, as it were, in the form of lead?"

"Oh, yes—it's still a collection of lino lines, headline castings and blocks wedged into a rigid steel frame. And the images on the lead itself are like 'looking glass' writing—negative impressions. In the next department, by various processes involving electric furnaces, a positive mould of this is taken in papier mâché. This is called the matrix. And finally the image is transferred back to negative when the matrix is used as a mould to make what is in effect one large block—but this last is in the form of a cylinder instead of being flat."

"And this, I suppose, is one of the rollers we see in those film cliché shots of the mighty presses rolling?"

"Exactly. The roller, in combination with others for other pages, is used on a rotary press to make the impressions *you* see when you open your paper. And how it would be possible to interrupt this—this progression, removing one part and sub-stituting another, we can try to find out below. Though I've an idea it's going to prove complicated . . ."

Lord Borridale led the way out from his apartment to the lifts. As they waited for the left-hand car to whine up from the ground floor, he pointed out items of interest which could

be seen through the great windows flanking the emergency
stairs twining round the shaft.

". . . faces towards the east, you see," he was saying. "Look,
there's the Old Bailey. And just beyond St. Paul's—beyond
that dreadful insurance building—you can see the tower of our
new . . ."

But Steed was not really listening. He was wondering whether
Lord Borridale knew that, among the Gustav Emmich geraniums
crowding the urn nearest his terrace table, there was concealed
a small microphone whose lead disappeared over the balustrade
and down the face of the building.

3

A SPEECH WITH A DIFFERENCE!

THE girl was tall—five foot eight at least, Steed guessed—and
she carried herself well. Cut in a thick, straight fringe reaching
almost to her eyebrows, her corn-coloured hair was worn short
and *bouffant*—a shallow gold bell tolling about her splendid
neck. Her legs were long and slender, her flanks sloping, and
her breasts, carried a little low on the rib-cage, the kind that
swing from side to side rather than bounce up and down with
exertion. She wore a tight skirt in Cape kid and a blinding
white blouse caught at the neck with a ridiculous black
velvet bow.

"Please come this way," she said expressionlessly, leading
Steed and Borridale to the Managing Editor's sanctum. They
passed through a comfortably furnished outer office with three
telephones, filing cabinets and a bank of teleprinters. On a low
table beside the desk, an earthenware jug held an unusual
mixture of arum lilies and red-hot pokers. The secretary knocked
at an inner door labelled *Robin Creighton—Private,* then stood
aside to let them pass as it was jerked open by a tall, fleshy
man resembling the actor, Charles Laughton.

"Come in, come in. Nice to see you, Basil," he said, shaking
hands with Borridale. "What d'you think of the latest, eh?
Poor old Sir George in the stocks again! And we're most
prominent among the clouds of witnesses . . ."

"As before, Rob; as before. But this time we're going to do
something about it. You know who I had lunch with—well,
he's sent us Mr Steed . . . Mr John Steed: Robin Creighton . . .
he's sent us Mr Steed to—er—to help clear things up a little.
Without betraying confidences or going too deeply into anything, I'll just say that I should be grateful if you could see your
way to hiring Mr Steed—on a purely temporary basis, of course,
so that he would have a reason for being here. I thought perhaps
you could fit him in among Warr's team . . . You do have a fair

amount of social contacts in the West End, Mr Steed?"

"Oh, one gets around, you know. One gets around," Steed murmured easily, looking for somewhere to put his hat and umbrella.

"We shall be glad to have you with us, Mr Steed," Creighton said, taking them from him and shaking hands. His handshake was limp and moist, like the lips he wrapped so lovingly around his words before sending them out into the world.

After a brief conversation covering much the same ground as his previous talk with Borridale, Steed asked: "Forgive my ignorance, but what exactly are the continental editions we are talking about?"

"Well, they're not special editions for the Continent," Creighton said. "And to that extent, perhaps, the term's a misnomer. Our first edition is put to bed—that is to say, it passes a point beyond which the editorial can no longer alter anything—at five thirty-eight, about an hour and a half from now. When it's printed, it goes—by plane, train or whatever— to foreign countries, to the Orkneys, the Shetlands, the Channel Isles, the Scillies and the West of Ireland. The far flung bits, in fact."

"Including the places we are considering?"

"Yes. The paper they get in Amsterdam, Paris, Rome and so on, is our normal first edition—or it should be! We print another at a quarter past eight, which goes to the north of Scotland, west Wales, the rest of Ireland and the West Country —incorporating any changes in the news which have broken since the first edition was printed, of course. Then there's the ten forty, mainly for the more accessible rural areas; the twelve thirty for provincial cities—and a late London edition in the early hours with real, up-to-the-minute stuff on the front page."

"I suppose the articles and features remain the same, but are the front pages of all five editions different?"

"It depends. Rarely, we might get a night when the same story ran throughout all five. Usually the top story in the earlier editions is superseded by a better one—perhaps from a part of the world where the day starts much later than ours. Even if we keep the same story, editors frequently improve its presentation or re-phrase the headline."

"So nobody is particularly surprised if a front page story is ripped out and another put in its place?"

"No. But that would hardly apply here, would it? The fake stories were substituted for reports in the *first* edition."

"And they only appeared in those bundles of the paper that were sent overseas—not in the first editions that went to . . . where did you say? . . . the Orkneys and so on?"

"Only those which were sold on continental mainland sites, to be precise."

"I see. Do you happen to have copies of the unadulterated first edition to compare with copies of the bogus one sold on the Continent?"

"Indeed. And copies of the other two papers involved, too, as it happens. I'll get them brought up—perhaps you'd like to see Lindale, the man who was long-stop on the night in question? He should be in today."

"Long-stop?"

"The sub-editor left on duty after all the rest have gone home —just in case there's been some frightful cock-up (in which case he has to fix it), or some news item of world-shattering importance breaks (in which case he has to decide whether or not to get the night editor out of bed!)."

Frank Lindale wore grey flannel trousers with turn-ups, a green shirt with the sleeves rolled up, and glasses. His short upper lip was spiked with an aggressively jutting moustache. "I've brought the home and away copies for you to see," he said almost truculently—was there a trace of Lancashire accent there, a hint of inferiority complex in the boldly staring blue eyes? "You can compare the two and you'll see that what happened to *us* was quite a different thing . . ."

Steed looked first at the two copies of the *Gazette*. In the "unadulterated" first edition, the report of Sir George Carew's speech at Grantham was on the back page—a two-inch single-column spot, below the fold, under the modest heading FOREIGN SECRETARY URGES EXPORT OVERHAUL. In the bogus edition sold on the Continent, the story was in exactly the same place, but the headline now read FOREIGN SECRETARY FLAYS EUROPEAN 'WASTERS', and the first paragraph of the copy had been altered to support the new title. The *Globe*'s story on the speech was even more perfunctory in treatment. Two paragraphs—a "squib" to fill up a hole at the bottom of a column on page five— that was all they had allowed it. But the same routine had been followed in the forged edition sold abroad. The headline now read CAREW CITES 'CONTINENTAL CON-MEN', and in the same position below this, there now appeared two paragraphs of explosive anti-European diatribe.

Alterations to the *Courier*'s first edition had been far more extensive. The unimportant speech story had been bodily removed from page two, and an equally banal item of local interest substituted in its place. The speech itself—or, rather, the "rewritten" version of it—had then been found another, more prominent position. "You may care to have a look at Kirwan's report on it," Lindale said. "I've clipped it there to the top . . ."

The report, typed on one of the *Courier*'s memorandum slips, said:

The faking has been on quite a big scale. As on the two previous occasions, the main front-page story has been removed, and, in its place, with scare headlines, a bowdlerised version of Sir George Carew's speech substituted.

The story itself has been cleverly handled—the memorandum went on—*in the main following the advance text of the speech circulated by the Minister's press office . . . but with significant differences. The judicious omission of an occasional negative, the substituting of pejorative for flattering epithets, the leaving as a statement of what was originally framed as a question . . . all these have altered beyond words the sense, and therefore importance, of the speech.*

"This phoney top story," Lindale said, "leads with two or three quotes that are pure fabrication—just to catch the eye, I suppose, and justify the headline. But there are a couple of good examples of the method used a few pars down . . . Look! There—the advance text says, 'The Italian people must be allowed to direct their own economy'. And that appears in the fake story as, '*Must* the Italian people be allowed to direct their own economy?' Then again—where he's talking about wartime friendships and all that—the text says, 'We must not forget what we owed the Dutch people; did they not fight as well as they could . . ?' and so on. And here it comes out as, 'We must forget what we owed the Dutch people; they did not fight as well as they could'."

"I must say, I see what you mean," Steed said. "One would never think the omission of one negative and the transposition of another would so completely pervert the meaning of a sentence!"

"How do you propose setting about elucidating the mystery, Mr Steed?" Creighton asked in his unctuous voice. "I mean, finding out where and how it is done . . . and, I suppose, why?"

"In the first instance," Steed replied crisply, "by asking questions—relevant and irrelevant, interesting and boring, informed and ignorant—all over the place! Let's just take your own paper. You say these alterations couldn't possibly have been made at editorial level—that is to say before the paper is printed?"

"Good God, no!" It was Lindale who replied. "In the first place, if that had been done the *whole* edition would have carried the alterations—the copies sold here in the U.K. as well as the continental ones. And, secondly, to do such a thing frankly involves far too many people. It would be virtually impossible to substitute a fake story like that without somebody finding out—unless practically the entire staff were in on it."

"He's right, of course, Mr Steed," Creighton said. "Think for a moment of the genuine top story—the one that was removed to make way for the fake. After being selected for that honourable position by a man we call the 'copytaster', probably in association with the news editor, it passes to a sub-editor who tailors it, in length and style, for the position and then sends it upstairs with his instructions to the print shop. The deputy Printer probably handles it, giving the text matter to one or more linotype operators to set, and the headlines to somebody else. The story then goes to the compositor who is making up that page and, when he has put it in position, it is proofed."

"Yes, I begin to see; it would certainly—"

"But wait, Mr Steed! *Before* the *page* is proofed, a galleyman has pulled proofs of the story itself. The galley proofs are seen by a proof reader, by the lawyer's department and possibly other people! Then the page proofs go again to the readers, to the sub who sent the story up, to the chief sub-editor and perhaps the night editor . . ."

"Obviously, then, it would be quite—"

"And even then the chain continues. Perhaps there are alterations to the story, to other stories on the page—or maybe even a substitution—in which case the entire process may be gone through again. Or at the least the stone sub has a look at it."

"The stone sub?"

"A sub-editor posted up on the stone—where the compositors make-up the pages, that is—to make any last-minute adjustments necessary before the edition is put to bed. He can do an on-the-spot job, where sending a proof down to the editorial department and waiting for it to come back, corrected, would hold up the schedule."

"I see."

"Now—with the possible exception of the operators and the galleyman—every single one of those people has contributed something to that page and therefore has a sort of fatherly interest in it. In addition, several of them have a special interest in the story itself. I ask you—is it reasonable, or even believable, that a whole, different story could go through without even one of them noticing?"

"Obviously not. Do you think, then—"

"Ah, but I can go further than that, Mr Creighton," Lindale interrupted. ". . . So sorry, Mr Steed . . . I happened to be on the stone for the whole shift last night, and I was in early so I saw every edition. We led with the housing story on the five-star and four-star—"

"Excuse me, I wonder—"

"Each edition is identified by the number of stars printed above the Stop Press box," Creighton supplied. "With us, the earliest edition has the most stars."

"Thank you."

"—then we changed the head for the three-star. And by the time the two-star was put to bed, the air crash had broken in Alaska so naturally we ripped out the housing and put that in instead. It stayed for the one-star, with a few supplementary details and eye witness bits."

"Was there a no-star yesterday?"

"No."

"Then it looks as though we're forced to the conclusion that the faking is done after the page—goes downstairs, you say, don't you?—after the page has left the shop to be made into a matrix, anyway?" Steed said. "Do any of you gentlemen have any ideas how *that* could be done?"

"Well, it's the same story, Mr Steed," the sub said. "It's hard to see just how that could be done either. I mean . . ."

"Was it Sherlock Holmes who said that one must eliminate the impossible and what remained—however improbable—

must be the truth?" Steed asked with a reflective smile curling his lip. "Don't you have some technique in the Street whereby changes to main stories or last-minute additions can be made in the middle of a run without actually having to start the whole process over again and make a new edition?"

"I expect you're thinking of slip editions or replates," the Managing Editor said, looking at him rather hard. "But there was no no-star yesterday."

"And anyway, the number of people who'd have to be in the know for an 'unofficial' replate would surely rule it completely out," Lindale objected. "Once the run's started, once the presses have begun to turn, it requires such a profusion of inter-related orders and counter-orders to stop it, that I should have thought that was quite out of the question."

"But is it *impossible*?" Steed pressed.

"Bearing in mind that, if it *was* done, all these people would have to be in on the conspiracy—and also bearing in mind their diverse social and professional strata—I'd say: Yes. It *is* impossible."

"I agree," Creighton nodded. "I agree."

"Well do you have any theories, then?"

"Told you twice, Steed—no, I haven't," Borridale said. "Nor has Robin here, or he'd have told us. I don't know about you, young man?"

"Well, it sounds completely crazy . . ." the sub hesitated.

"'What remains, *however improbable*, must be true'," Steed quoted softly.

"Yes, well— Well, *I* think the only way it could even begin to be feasible would be to substitute the mats," Lindale said defensively.

"Substituting matrices!"

"Yes, Mr Creighton. Look—your page forme (that's a steel frame holding the lead making up two complementary pages, Mr Steed) . . . your forme goes into your furnace flat. We've agreed it's the right one when it goes in. What comes out the other end?—A papier mâché mould. At the beginning it's flat, easily transportable, difficult to read unless you look hard —at what other time do you have a better chance of making a substitution?"

"Ye-e-es. That may be an idea, Lindale. But . . ."

"Look," the young man urged, "we agree that too many

people would be involved for it to get done before the page goes into the furnace. And we say too many different *kinds* of people would be involved for it to be done once the run starts—that is, once the mat has become the roller. The short space in between furnace and roller happens also to coincide with the point when the thing's easiest to handle."

"Even so—"

"I mean, you can't go lugging formes all over the place: it takes a couple of chaps even to slide one. Same for your roller. But a spare mat could so easily be lost—there's always masses of spoiled ones lying around anyway."

"How many people would need to be involved?"

"A few—it couldn't be done single-handed. The two men who do the make-ready, at least one around the furnace. Perhaps another to bring the bogus mat . . ."

"Young man, I think you have something there," Borridale said, taking out his notebook and writing busily.

Steed coughed. He placed an elegant ankle across an expensively covered knee and grasped it with both hands. "You'll forgive the insertion of a merely lay opinion, I hope?" he drawled. "But what about the time element?"

"The time element?"

"Yes. Presumably the spurious matrix is exactly the same as the genuine one with the exception of the top story which has been substituted?"

"That's right."

"And the fake will have been made, like the real one, in a furnace from a forme—is that what you call it?—a forme prepared by a compositor?"

"Yes."

"And the forme contains two complementary pages—in this case, since the one we're dealing with is the front page, I suppose the other one in the forme is the back page?"

"That's correct Mr Steed."

"Well this is my question. As front pages and so on are kept to the last minute, so that the very latest news can be put in, *how do the fakers get sight of the genuine pages long enough before edition time to prepare facsimiles, with all the setting and compositing and proof reading that this entails?*"

There was a short silence.

Then, "That's—er—a very good question, Mr Steed,"

Lindale said at last. "You're quite right. These are not feature pages, prepared hours—or even a day—before. They only receive their final shape minutes before edition time. Even if they had proofs available, no forgers, however expert, could produce another two-page forme in anything like the time at their disposal here—quite apart from the fact that they'd have to have lino operators, comps, make-ready men and I don't know what-all else available. That seems to knock my little idea on the head all right!"

Steed grinned. "Sorry," he said. "It doesn't mean that's not the point where the mischief *is* done; only that perhaps it's not done that way."

Creighton was staring at Steed again. "I must confess myself dazzled by your—ah—sudden grasp of the principles of newspaper manufacture, Mr Steed," he said levelly.

Steed ran a finger and thumb along the impeccable crease of his trouser leg. "Oh, one listens and learns from the best sources," he said vaguely.

Lord Borridale was clearly amused. He gave a little bark of laughter. "Well, at least we can agree on a couple of things for the moment," he said. "One, we think that this must be the work of a conspiracy—however it's actually done—rather than the work of a single crooked man. Two, on balance of probability—or should I say *im*probability, Mr Steed?—we agree that Mr Lindale's theory gives us the most *likely* time at which any substitution could be affected. The problem now is —how to stop it happening again."

Steed rose to his feet. "With respect, Lord Borridale," he said, "that's not the problem at all."

"Oh," said his lordship blankly, "isn't it? What is then?"

The special agent walked to the window and looked out for a moment before replying. On the flat roof of a building across the road, two girls in black lace brassieres sat with their backs against a chimney stack, sunbathing. "It would be quite easy," Steed said slowly at last, "to post enough spies about to stop anyone doing this again. But the point is, one wouldn't really scotch it at all, simply by making it too difficult to do again. The person or persons involved would just find some other equally ingenious way of ruining the country's image."

"You think that's the ultimate aim of the operation?" Borridale said.

"Undoubtedly. It doesn't matter that we can prove the words were not really said. The thing engenders lack of confidence, loss of prestige, general tarnishing of the old image, you know."

"To whose advantage?"

"Could be many people. Economic rivals abroad. Political rivals. Spheres-of-influence rivals. Ideological rivals. Even certain classes of person at home could stand to gain in certain circumstances. But the point is, as I said, that the *continuance* of this image-spoiling must be prevented. In other words, the whole scheme has to be exposed, its working laid bare and its protagonists caught, as they say, red-handed."

"And you propose to do this by letting them have another go? It *will* happen again, the newspaper faking, I mean?"

"Oh, yes." Steed said easily. "It'll happen again."

"You seem very sure."

"It has to, Lord Borridale. Since the Foreign Secretary isn't really saying these things, people will cotton on soon enough that it's some kind of racket. The only point *can* be to create the maximum confusion in the minimum time—that is, the fakers have to keep on and on, achieving their effect by cumulative means."

One of the telephones on Creighton's desk shrilled imperatively.

"Excuse me," he said, lifting the receiver to his ear. "Hallo? Yes. Yes — all right, Sandra, I haven't forgotten. Thank you. Yes—I'll be down in a couple of minutes . . . Thank you."

He turned to his proprietor. "We have that meeting with the various union chapels, you remember, Basil?" he said. "You'll forgive us, Mr Steed; we have to go down to a round-table meeting on the subject of all-night canteen facilities . . ."

In the outer office, he took hold of his secretary by one forearm and brought her forward. "Steed," he said, "I'd like you to meet my secretary, Sandra Gillan. Sandra—Mr Steed will be working with us for a while on Warr's column. Perhaps you'd be good enough to take him down and find him a desk and a typewriter . . ?"

The girl looked somehow harassed. A lock of her golden hair had come adrift and now stuck up above her head, rising and falling as she walked. Evidence of exertion shadowed a half circle beneath one arm of her shirt, and there was a white smudge at the hip where her leather skirt had brushed too close to a wall.

"Oh, Lindale," she said when Borridale and Creighton had gone, "I wonder would you mind . . ? Your desk is so near Mr Warr's; perhaps you'd be kind enough to take down Mr—Steel was it?—on your way . . ?"

"Steed, actually. I was wondering whether perhaps one might suggest a little something in the way of a noggin, you know," Steed said. "Just to celebrate my appointment. I happen to know rather a nice little club just off Long Acre . . ."

"Yes, I could take a half hour, I suppose," Lindale said dourly. "I wouldn't mind a pint."

Steed looked expectantly at Sandra Gillan. The tall blonde shook her head. She pushed the out-of-place lock of hair back with one hand. "No thank you, Mr—er—Steed," she said coolly. "I've rather a lot to catch up on. And anyway I mustn't leave my post." She stared at the sub-editor for a moment and then turned on her heel and walked back into Creighton's office, the dark nylons swishing as her magnificent thighs scissored beneath the tight skirt.

Lindale and Steed raised eyebrows at one another and then strode off down the corridor towards the lifts. As they were waiting for the car to come up—"We'll take the left-hand one," Lindale said; "the middle one's the slowest!"—the special agent became aware of a faint pounding, felt rather than heard, far below his feet. Floors below them, the great rotary machines were in action, the presses had begun to roll.

Noticing Steed's reaction, the sub looked automatically at his watch. "Ah, yes," he said. "The five-star. They've started to run the edition . . ."

4

DEATH ON A HOT NIGHT

THE chest and shoulders of John Steed were muscular without lacking grace. At a quarter past one that morning, he bared them to the stream of tepid air directed towards him by an electric fan on his bookcase. At one twenty, his trousers joined the shirt, singlet and tie already on the floor at the foot of the divan. Twenty-six minutes past one saw him heave an exasperated sigh, sit cross-legged on his cushions and raise the heavy text book he had been trying to read in an attempt to help the fan agitate the heavy air. Before the little Napoleonic barrel clock on the desk had stated its silvery half hour, he was under the shower trying to persuade himself that the water cascading over his body was ice-cold.

Two things happened simultaneously then. He looked down and away from the bright, dancing jets of water to discover that he was still wearing silk socks and a pair of suede Chelsea boots in a particularly delicate shade of grey.

And the telephone in the living room began to ring.

Steed permitted himself an imprecation in Turkish. He slammed off the shower, snatched a blue bath sheet in towelling from the same source and squelched his way, wrapping this around his wet body, to the desk.

"Hallo? Steed? . . . Didn't know if you'd be in yet. Been out myself all evening and only just got back to find your message on the answering machine . . ." It was Borridale—sounding happy and well entertained.

"How nice of you to call back. Good evening," Steed replied, stealthily trying to dry his chest, stop his improvised sarong from falling off and hold the receiver at the same time. Water dripped from his nose and chin on to the tooled Morocco top of the desk.

"Anyway, what can I do for you now that we have got in touch?" his lordship continued.

37

"It wasn't really important. I just wondered if you knew that your Gustav Emmich geraniums were bugged—I hardly liked to tell you in front of the other people and then you went off with Creighton."

"What's that you say? Bugged? They can't be. Why I sprayed them myself only this morning."

Steed coughed. "A technical term. Bugged. There was a microphone hidden in them . . ."

"A microphone! In the geraniums?"

"Yes . . . When I called on you today . . ."

"You're joking, Steed!"

"I'm afraid not, Lord Borridale."

"Well, I'm blessed! Is it still there?"

"I was rather hoping—if it isn't too late, that is—that you might totter out and have a look."

"'Totter' is right. I'll go right away . . . Bugged, eh? Oh, well: I suppose you people have your shop just as we do. A microphone in *my* geraniums . . ." The voice faded into the distance.

Steed looked past the trail of moist footprints across his carpet, past the three steps leading down to the lower level of his sitting room, past the tiger-skin rug and the glass case of hunting trophies to the rosewood sideboard. The soda siphon resting on its polished top still wore a misting of condensation from the refrigerator. Beads of moisture slid lazily down the silver bucket holding what was left of the ice. The relationship between the tall, green, empty glass and the short, brown, full whisky bottle cried out, Steed felt, for adjustment. If he put down the receiver for a moment . . .

"Steed?" The voice of the *Courier*'s proprietor barked in his ear. "I don't see any dam' microphone in my geraniums. Not a sign of one."

"No, I didn't think you would," the undercover man murmured.

"Eh? What's that? What's that?"

"I hardly thought it would still be there. There *was* one this afternoon, though. Thanks for looking . . . It's interesting: that proves that the flowers were bugged for one special purpose only—to overhear your conversation with me . . ."

"Were they, by Jove! You're sure of that?"

"Absolutely. You'll let me know if you—er—come across any more, won't you?"

"Certainly, Mr Steed. And you'll let *me* know if *you* come across any microphones in *your* flat, won't you?" Borridale said with a chuckle.

"It'll be a pleasure," Steed said lazily. He dropped the receiver back on its cradle, switched off the tape machine which had been automatically recording their conversation, and started for the siphon.

The telephone rang again instantly.

He sighed and picked it up again. "Hallo? Yes?"

"Hallo? Mr Steed?"

"Yes; who is it?"

"Mr *John* Steed?"

"Yes."

"*Courier* switchboard here, Mr Steed . . . Hold on a minute, please. I have a call for you . . ."

Steed eyed the siphon wistfully as he waited. His glance roamed the big, comfortable room and fell on the book he had been reading—now lying open where he had left it on the divan.

papers have different systems of identifying for their own purposes the various editions (he read without thinking from the top of the page). *In some cases this is effected by the number of small stars or 'solid circles' visible in a predetermined, inconspicuous place. In others, small letters or numerals are used. One famous newspaper uses a device even simpler: there is a minute break in the rule underlining the title on the front page—and the farther to the left the break occurs, the earlier the edition . . .*

The telephone clicked loudly in his ear. "Mr Steed?"—the voice was Frank Lindale's, urgent and excited—"Hope I didn't disturb you . . ?"

"Not at all," Steed said pleasantly. "I was just reading Kennedy Smiley, as a matter of fact, on *The Production And Management Of Newspapers.*"

"Ah, yes! It's the only one! A splendid text book, Mr Steed . . . splendid. Yet there are other books equally interesting from a different point—Mr Steed! Could you possibly come down here? To the *Courier*?"

"Now?"

"Yes, now. I know it's terribly late and all that, but—well, I think I'm on to something. Something important."

"Something to do with the little matter we were discussing in Mr Creighton's office earlier today?"

"Indeed. I'd like to show you . . . something."

"And you can't tell me over the phone?"

"Not really. I—I'd rather—well, I'd just rather not, if you don't mind, Mr Steed. I think it might be . . . better . . . if you came here."

"And it won't wait until the morning?"

"Well, I know it's a bit of a liberty, asking you to come out at this time, but—no, *I* don't think it will wait."

"All right," Steed decided with characteristic abruptness. "I'll be with you in twenty minutes. Where exactly are you?"

"Thanks. I'm on the stone. That's on the fourth floor. Ask for Len—Len Fowles, the Deputy Printer—he'll show you where I am."

Steed finally made the whisky and siphon before the last of the ice went, showered his damp body with talc, drew on a pair of thin black trousers and a stone-coloured T-shirt in feather-weight Shetland, and went to find some dry shoes. Two minutes later he was standing at the foot of what he liked to call his back stairs—the space-saving wrought-iron spiral which dropped straight from his kitchen to the garage beneath. The thin, acrid, aromatic tang of petrol, the bland smell of polish-ed leather upholstery and the close, oily odour of the place itself washed over him in the hot night as he paused an instant to drink in the classic lines of the motor car gleaming there.

In an era increasingly preoccupied with the ephemeral, the disposable and the transient, items persist nevertheless from an age of craftsmanship—not as curiosities behind glass but as everyday, working objects whose superb original design and construction permits them still to compete with (and occasion-ally even excel) the automated products of today. Such a splendid anachronism was Steed's barrel clock; such were the eighteenth-century desk upon which it stood, the Fox frame to his favourite umbrella, a cast-iron Victorian juicer which was quicker and more prolific of the healing draught than any electric fruit blender. And such a one was the 4½-litre Bentley on whose shining green side his hand now rested. Designed and built by W. O. Bentley in 1930, lovingly restored in 1947 by H. M. Mackenzie, cherished for some years now by Steed himself and always in showroom condition, the great car was a text-book example of the thoroughbred elegance whom age does not wither nor custom stale (its owner was fond of saying). No such "sporting" vulgarities as outside exhausts, a slab tank or a truncated two-seater body had been permitted to defile the matchless touring coachwork by Vanden Plas, with its long, raking front wings and simple four-seater tonneau. The sole concession to *la course* was that, over the supercharger housing, the enormous Gothic-arch radiator carried—to team with those covering the big headlamps—a chromed mesh stoneguard. Steed lifted one side of the imperious bonnet to tickle the carburetter. The engine was gigantic—a symphony of brass-work, aluminium, steel and polished copper filling the space from radiator core to scuttle, from bonnet hinge almost to the ground.

He pressed a wall button to operate the electric gates sealing off the garage from the mews, opened the shallow door on the car's near side and slid across the squat, hand-made bucket seat into the driving position, where he stretched his long legs across the flat floor to the pedals. Dropping his right hand to ease off the brake, he started the engine and coaxed the short, heavy, right-hand gear lever into first.

Not long afterwards, he was bowling along Whitehall in third, the contralto whine of the Bentley's close-ratio gearbox contrasting agreeably with the deep, "separated" burble of its two-and-a-half-inch exhaust.

Steed drove expertly and without fuss—a shade of panache intruding from time to time to cloud faintly what a purist would otherwise concede to be an impeccable technique. The long-stroke engine was in fact flexible enough to cope with most late-night traffic conditions in third or top, but it was difficult to resist the temptation to whip down through the superb box every time it was necessary to slow or stop. And as for the stalled Mini-Cooper at the Trafalgar Square traffic lights, Steed himself would have maintained that he leaned out and down to rap on its rooftop simply to enquire if he could be of any help . . .

At the *Courier* building, he drove smartly straight into the space labelled *Mr Robin Creighton* and switched off the Bentley's engine. It was just seventeen minutes since he had spoken to Frank Lindale on the telephone.

Nine out of ten doormen allow to pass without question the

man whose arrogance is sufficiently marked, whose autocratic air implies familiarity with the building and brooks no hindrance. The night men at the *Courier* were no exceptions and Steed strode without hesitation across the foyer to the left-hand lift, pressed the button and, while he waited for the car to come down from the eighth floor, turned round to nod a cool goodnight to them.

A messenger on the fourth floor took him to Len Fowles— a grey man in a grey suit separating a pile of typescript into 100-word takes and distributing them to linotype operators through numbered pigeonholes above his desk. "Frank Lindale?" he said. "He was over there on four with Arthur—but he had to go downstairs a while ago."

"Downstairs?"

"Yes, sir. He was waiting for Arthur to flop the foot of the page when there was this phone call—"

"Phone call?" Steed repeated, the tiny alarm bells ringing wildly in his head. "Who called him? Where did he go?"

"I've no idea. The phone rang here on my desk, and it was for him, so I called him over."

"You didn't hear what he said?"

"I wasn't paying much attention. Come to think of it, he hardly said anything at all. Just listened and then said, right, he'd be down."

"And you've no idea where he went?"

"Ah, wait a minute! I never said that, sir. I said I didn't know *who* it was rang him. I know where he *went*: he told me. He went down to the machine room . . ."

Inexplicably a prey to sudden fear, Steed whirled and ran along the passage to the lifts. The left-hand one was back at the eighth floor. The centre car was only at the floor below.

He pressed the button to call the middle one.

Once inside, fretting with impatience, he thought he saw why everyone on the *Courier* preferred the other: this lift certainly *seemed* to be taking an age to glide to the ground floor. "Machine room?" he called crisply as the door slid open at the entrance hall.

"One more down, sir," a porter called back. "The street's a storey lower where the vans go, at the back. But *we* call it the basement!"

Steed pressed the button inside the lift again. At the floor below, he catapulted out into the thunder of machinery, the flat, sour smell of metal and grease, the clanking of iron arms. Beyond the moving kaleidoscope of steel, vast doors stood open to the sultry night.

There was hardly a soul on the concrete floor of the huge shop: minders, apprentices, machine-men and clickers—they were all gathered in an uneasy knot, crowded below the arc lights in the loading bay beside the doors. As he ran over, the palisade of legs shifted and moved, the frozen tableau melted and re-formed . . . They were surrounding something that lay on the ground. One of the great rolls of newsprint bulked against the darkness a yard away, its paper coverings stained and horrible in the pitiless light. Nearer, a shape sprawled grotesquely in the dust. There was a great deal of blood—and from the centre projected an outflung arm, a green shirtsleeve rolled to the elbow. Distinguishable on the far side were grey flannel trouser legs with turn-ups. The feet, pathetic and child-like in death, turned toe-inwards beyond them.

Steed was too late. Somebody else had got to Frank Lindale first.

5

A PART FOR EMMA PEEL

FEW people ever saw Emma Peel's bed. Like the rest of the furniture and fittings in the room in which she slept, it remained concealed behind the sycamore panelling to be summoned forth at the push of a button. There were a lot of buttons, arranged in rows on a wooden platen screwed to the wall. Some of them had red, blue or green indicator lights to show when the fitting to which they related was in use. Like an organist at the console, Emma used the buttons to arrange the big, airy room to suit her mood or her needs: chairs, lamps, the bed, a magazine rack, television, even a massage table could be produced noiselessly from their hidden, dustproof recesses at the stab of a finger.

There was a luxurious bathroom suite at one side of the room, a short passage leading to the kitchen and the living room on the other. The kitchen was small but it had been designed by an expert in ergonomics. Around the hooded, modernistic fireplace in the centre, the living room, too, deployed a *persona* as streamlined and up-to-the-minute as Emma's own.

From it, with courage, intelligence and a certain quiet desperation, Emma had directed her personal campaign to re-establish a life shattered by the death of her husband—an ace pilot killed testing a supersonic aircraft.

Now, at 27, a woman of independent means, she could afford to indulge a diversity of hobbies acquired during an education on the Continent and in South America, and on her travels with her father, who had been Sir John Knight, the shipping magnate.

The studio whose windows gave on to her roof garden was filled with evidence of her interest and her talent—from oil painting to collecting porcelain, from textile design to the paper on mediaeval history whose final page was still in her typewriter.

Emma Peel herself was in the press-button bed when the

telephone rang that evening. The first hammer-stroke on the bell broke a circuit and the instrument slid easily out from behind a movable panel on an extension, to be waiting automatically by the bedside when she struggled awake.

"Mrs Peel?" The voice was familiar; unidentifiable for a second.

"Who is it?"

"Steed here. John Steed. Sorry to ring so late but we must talk."

"Steed!" Surprise, pleasure, a touch of apprehension—suspicion even?—warred for ascendancy in her warm but decisive voice. "Where are you? What are you doing? And to what do I owe the pleasure of this unexpected call?"

The undercover man laughed softly. "To answer your curiosity in the sequence in which it was expressed," he said, responding to the implicit challenge in Emma's voice, "in a public call box off Fleet Street; working late on a little job—and offering you a job, too!"

"That would be nice. Perhaps you could drop around tomorrow—"

"I'm afraid it means you would have to come out—tonight."

"Oh. Very well. I'll—Steed! Do you know it's two thirty? I've just looked at my watch! Are you joking?"

"Never more serious, my dear. Put on some clothes and meet me in the West End."

"What sort of clothes? Meet you where?"

"At the—let's see . . . I think a spot of class wouldn't come amiss, as they say in the strip cartoons . . . Yes. Meet me at the Argosy."

"A night club? I shall have to dress formally."

"That will be your loss and my gain. In a half hour?"

"I suppose so," Emma grumbled good-naturedly. "Though why you—"

"Splendid! See you downstairs," Steed said, and rang off.

Emma shrugged her wide, slim shoulders and pressed the button marked wardrobe. Of the mass of efficient gadgetry in the top-floor Hampstead flat, the wardrobe was the most completely Emma. The button actuated sliding doors which withdrew from one complete wall—but behind these, movable perspex screens still guarded the clothes themselves, leaving the button-presser simply to work an inclined switchboard resembling the control panel of a juke-box. This was a wardrobe computer, a tolerably uncomplicated electronic device which assessed data on climate, temperature, time of day, etc., fed into it, and then disgorged a selection of clothing appropriate to the occasion. "It's as though Emma subconsciously resents the science that took away her husband," Flavia Lyall, the biologist, who had been at school with her, once said. "And now, to get her own back, she *uses* science—makes *it* work for her . . ."

Pausing now with index finger suspended over the switches, Emma pondered the information to feed in. There were six selector panels labelled "Season", "Time of Day", "Occasion", "Temperature", "Humidity" and "Classification". Each panel carried a number of buttons with categories listed against them, and she had no hesitation in pressing those indicating *Summer*, *Night* and *Formal* on the first three panels. "Temperature" was presumably *Hot*, she considered; and to her at any rate the humidity was *High*. She was uncertain about the last—but at length, with a slight smile and another shrug, she stabbed the button marked * * * * *.

There was a subdued whirring within the machine, the sound of selectors engaging. Tumblers dropped. Then a perspex door slid aside at the far end of the wall and three matched ensembles jerked into the room on extension arms for her to choose from.

Steed—who had been home to change and was now impeccable in charcoal—had his back to the stairs when she came into the Argosy. But he knew she had arrived by the turning of heads, rippling the night-club's clientele like a breeze in a corn-field. Emma was tall, with a slender, curvaceous figure and those special hips which are wide, sloping and generous viewed from the front or back—and as slim as a boy's seen from the side. She was wearing hipster pants in ice blue lamé, with a loose jacket of the same material swinging open to reveal a matching bikini bra above her long, creamy torso. Her auburn hair, drawn backwards and upwards from her wide forehead and enormous brown eyes, accentuated the almost slavic planes of her face.

Steed was on his feet before she reached the table. "Mrs Peel!" he beamed, ushering her to a chair, "How nice. How very nice of you to come! And how delightful . . . you're quite the coolest-looking thing here—and you can take that any way you like . . ."

The graceful head inclined in acceptance of this compliment. Beneath the straight nose, the mouth blossomed like a peony in the midst of the alabaster skin. "Come off it, Steed," Emma Peel said crisply. "What have you brought me here for at this time of night?"

"But my dear—for the stimulation of your delightful company, of course," the undercover man murmured. "I could think of nothing more suitable for a thundery summer night in London than a bottle of *Gewürztraminer* from the Domaine of Bollenberg—do you remember, we visited it once when we worked on that job at Rouffach in Alsace?—so I've asked them to chill some for us. It'll be here in a moment. I do hope that's to your liking?"

"I'm waiting, Steed," the girl said. She looked briefly around the downstairs room. The Argosy boasted a fashionable *discothèque*, noisy, expensive and overcrowded, at street level; down here, the money talked more discreetly. There was a great deal of red plush, Regency wallpaper, gilt and crystal. Most of the tables were alcoved off around a central space housing more tables, a diminutive dance floor and a trio playing sad Greek music on *bouzoukis*. It was the kind of place where the more serious actors, the more enlightened politicians, film directors and TV pundits, and the better class of publishers came to talk shop without being stared at.

"Ah! Here we are," Steed exclaimed as a waiter brought their wine. "Yes, that's just about right, thank you—you can tell your *sommelier* that he's one of the few left in London who doesn't over-cool his white wines . . . I say, isn't that an *entrancing* tune? I do so much prefer Greek pops—surely that's a Hadjidakis number?"

"Steed!" The voice was soft but the warning note was there.

"Oh, very well." He sighed. "Your good health, my dear. All right. Well, it seems that some person or persons unknown— almost certainly the latter—is or are making free with the freedom of the press."

"I'm sorry: I'm not quite with you."

Briefly, succinctly, he told her of his luncheon engagement, the conversation at the *Courier*, and what had happened since—

ending with his discovery of Lindale's death.

"But how horrible!" Emma exclaimed. "Are you sure it was murder?"

"I think it has to be. I've arranged a particularly hasty post-mortem—but I'm pretty sure of the result: we'll find that he was dead or unconscious before the—er—accident occurred."

"How *did* it occur?"

"It was most unfortunate—to quote an understatement of one of the machine room men—a most unfortunate accident. One of those huge rolls of newsprint the lorries deliver must have been insecurely fastened, I was told; and the chain must have come loose as it was swung from vehicle to loading bay. And of course the unfortunate fellow happened to be standing underneath at the time."

"Do you believe that?"

"No. Frankly, I don't. Nobody could explain to me what on earth a night sub could have been doing, standing underneath a loading bay at two o'clock in the morning. And even if he had been, one finds it hard to believe that he wouldn't have heard something and jumped out of the way."

"What about the phone call?"

"The phone call could have got him down to the machine room; but it's hard to imagine what could have been said to place him under a roll of paper being unloaded from a lorry. Especially as he was in the middle of a spell of work on the stone at the time."

"You haven't found out who made the call—or why?"

"No. Nobody admits to having made a call at all. Obviously his conversation with me must, at least in part, have been overheard. And he was killed to stop him showing me whatever it was that he'd found. The call, therefore, was simply a ruse to decoy him downstairs."

"And the switchboard don't remember? There can't be many calls at that time of night."

"There aren't. If it *had* gone through them, they would have remembered from what extension it was made. But it didn't—like most big firms, the *Courier* has an internal system. Direct dialling. And the call was on the internal phone, not the GPO extension."

"If he was knocked out and left lying there, and then the roll was deliberately dropped on him, it seems odd that nobody noticed. I've worked on newspapers—and there's always a great gang of people around."

"I know," Steed said soberly. "That's what frightens me. It brings the conspiracy element I told you about right in to the foreground. If that's what happened, quite a few of those men there *have* to be implicated."

Emma drank some wine. Steed refilled her glass and his own. Then, "Well—what about the job I've got to do, then?" Emma asked. "Is it a tail? Do I go to the *Courier*? Have I to follow somebody from here?"

"Job?" Steed sounded vague.

"Yes, Steed. J-O-B, job. You got me out of bed and brought me here because you had a job for me to do—or so you said."

"Of course. Stupid of me. Of course I had, my dear."

"Well, what is it?"

"Well, it seems to me that if somebody did kill Lindale because of what he was going to show or tell me, that same person must have overheard some or all of the telephone conversation Lindale had with me. Otherwise he'd never have known there was anything to show."

"Obviously."

"And it follows that it's quite likely he heard not only what Lindale said—but also to whom he said it. The young man did address me by name at least once. And that, in turn, means that my cover may be blown before I've even started . . . I can't loaf around hoping to pick something up like an ordinary staff member. They'll keep mum if I'm around, because they'll know I'm investigating the thing."

"Well?"

"So I thought the thing to do would be to plant a second string. Somebody intelligent, brave, blessed with plenty of initiative—"

"Steed!"

"—who could be given a staff job *pro tem*—perhaps attached to the beauty editor, say—and could have a well-formed ear to the—"

"*Steed!* Listen to me. Are you trying to tell me that you have arranged for me to join the staff of the *Courier*?"

"As special assistant to the beauty editor, I rang up Borridale just before you arrived! The money's quite good."

"Starting when?" Emma's voice was dangerously quiet.

"Well—er—tomorrow morning actually, I'm afraid. But you

don't have to be in until ten, you know. And it's two hours for lunch—"

"D'you mean to tell me that you woke me out of a deep sleep, got me out of bed, made me shower, dress, put on a face, come all the way down here at nearly three o'clock in the morning . . . just to tell me about a job that starts *tomorrow*?"

"The computer's to be congratulated. You look marvellous. Great talent, that—to be able to think that up in the early hours. The machine has a future."

"It offers a selection only," Emma said icily. "The actual choice is made by me. And you brought me here in the middle of the night, I say, when you could just as easily have telephoned me before breakfast—or even come to see me, if you weren't so lazy . . ."

"Much better to put you in the picture while the iron's hot. Besides, I might get assassinated in the night, and then nobody'd know a thing about it all."

"I should think it very likely. Any night. Of all the callous, egocentric, selfish—"

"Waiter!" Steed called urgently, getting to his feet. "My bill, please. The lady's leaving . . ."

6

"TURNING OVER AN OLD LEAF"

THE coffee had got quite cold by the time John Steed found what he wanted in the last of the heavy reference books from the Louis XVI *bibliothèque* beside his desk. But he was whistling to himself as he went out to the kitchen to grind some more. "Knew I'd seen it somewhere," he mused aloud, putting the Cona with its cargo of fresh coffee and water over the electric element. "Of course it's *Hemming's*. Should have recognised it at once . . ."

He returned to the living room, collected the book and a piece of torn, crumpled paper lying beside it, and carried them both back into the bedroom. He was still wearing the short, Cossack-style sleeping garment in prune silk which it pleased him to call a nightshirt. Once again settled in his favourite position, sitting cross-legged on the pillows, he took a final look at the reference book entry before smoothing out the paper and giving it his full attention.

It was the one positive clue he had found at the scene of Lindale's death: the sub had been holding it, screwed up into a ball in one clenched fist. Steed had managed to prise it out undetected and discovered, as soon as he was able to look at it alone, that it was a page—or part of a page—from a book. It had been a normal octavo-size volume, and the page was torn diagonally across so that the top, including the part where the title would normally be repeated, was missing. The text appeared to be nothing but a list of newspapers and periodicals with their names and addresses. At first, he had thought it must be from an index or a bibliography to some work—but then he had noticed that the two sides of the leaf were numbered 65 and 66, which seemed to rule this out: the pagination was too far advanced for anything in the nature of a contents list; not far enough on to be at the back of a book.

The first complete line on the torn page read: *Carver's*

Weekly (Fri.). Brock Publishing Ltd., 2 Quell Street, Edinburgh 3. (1s.) And underneath this, Steed saw:

    Carnwellian, the (Monthly, 1st) B. J. Beddoes Ltd., Port Road, Erith (Kent) (2s. 6d.)

    Charts and Maps (Quarterly) Navigational Society, London W.1 (£1)

    Clarion, the (Monthly. 10th) Clarion Press, Padstow, Cornwall (3s.)

    CLARION *(Hanningford) (Daily. Evg.) Olympus Press, Canal Street. Hanningford (Leics.) (3d.)*

    **Cooks And Chefs Weekly (Wed.) Wesker Press, Southwold (Suffolk)*

    Coronet *(Weekly. Wed.) Photodine Press, Fleet Street, London W.1 (1s. 3d).*

    CHURCHMAN, the (Weekly. Sun.) Geo. Harsh Press, London E.C.4 (6d.)

    Cow Breeder's Times (Bi-monthly) J. Piggot Ltd., Exeter, Devon (9d.)

He had puzzled over the entries for some time the previous night and it was only after nearly an hour's research this morning that he had finally identified the book from a bibliography of bibliographies. The page had been torn from *Hemming's Press Guide,* an expensive annual publication which was in fact a comprehensive listing of the world's newspapers, magazines and periodicals, complete with details of publishers, address, publication date, price and so on.

The guide was well-known among journalists, especially freelances; more so in the offices of advertising agencies and publicists, who found it invaluable for compiling their mailing lists. It was therefore feasible that Lindale might have been consulting a copy for reasons unconnected with his telephone call to Steed. On the other hand, two further possibilities could equally plausibly be argued: that he had found something of interest and torn out the page containing it, with the intention of giving this to Steed; or that the book had been torn out of his hand when and if he was attacked because it did have something to do with the forged newspaper reports. What it boiled down to was this: was this particular piece of paper a clue, a message deliberately left by the dead man to act as a pointer either to what he had found out or to his killers?

Or was the whole thing a coincidence, a red herring?

Before he could consider the matter any further, the telephone rang. It was the police doctor attached to the Special Branch reporting the result of the autopsy on Frank Lindale. "There's no doubt about it, I'm afraid," he said. "It's a case of murder. The man had been attacked and beaten before the bale of paper dropped on him."

"Was he dead before it dropped on him?"

"We can't tell definitely: there's too little margin, time-wise. You yourself were talking to him on the phone less than twenty minutes before his death. He would certainly have been unconscious."

"And the weapon?"

"Blunt instrument. An iron bar or something."

"I see. You'd better rephrase your opening remark, then."

"How d'you mean?"

"You said he was unconscious—or, rather, that he'd been attacked and beaten—before the bale of paper dropped on him. That should be rephrased to say before the bale of paper *was* dropped on him."

"Oh, yes. I see what you mean. Yes, I suppose that does follow."

"Definitely. Would you do me a favour, though? Would you please ask MacCorquodale if he'd kindly sit on the murder angle for a few days? You know—no enquiries, no follow-ups, accept the thing at its face value as an accident. If necessary swing an inquest verdict. I'll deal with the formalities and get official sanction for him . . ."

Another thing he would have to do, now that he knew for certain that Lindale had been murdered, was to base his actions on the assumption that the page of *Hemming's* was indeed in some way a clue or a message—so thought Steed as he put down the telephone and carried the crumpled piece of paper back to his bed. Had it been torn in a random or in a special way? Was any message implicit in this particular page? Or just in the book it had been torn from? Had the particular list of papers on each side of the page any special significance— Had those on the *other* portion of the ripped leaf, for that matter? He would have to get a complete copy of the guide and see what he could find. And he would also have to explore every possibility for implicit or explicit messages in the piece he had. Steed was an expert code-breaker and cryptographer. He sighed and reached for a pad of paper and a pencil.

The coffee bubbled away in the Cona. It was just eleven fifteen.

At eleven thirty, the coffee trolleys were wheeled around the editorial floors of the *Courier*. Emma Peel grasped the thick mug of tasteless fluid with relief. At least it was hot enough to scald her awake—and anything was better than this dreadful nodding off, this agonising struggle simply to stay awake until the woman whose assistant she was supposed to be made her appearance at eleven forty-five. Emma had a slight headache, a muzzy sense of malaise behind the eyes—and the day seemed to be hotter than ever. The dispirited leaves of a plane tree drooped heavy and listless in the still air outside the windows of the huge newsroom. The sunshine was brassy and even the shadows seemed to suffer from the blare of the heat.

Beside her, Samantha Sheppard, the big, healthy 20-year-old who had found a place for her on the Beauty desk, perspired quietly into a cotton print and favoured her with a desultory commentary on the *Courier*'s editorial department in between vetting a pile of press handouts on the lookout for possible copy.

"That's Ropey Curtis, the news editor—the little fat man at the end with all the paper on his private desk. The long table this side of him is the subs' table ... that's Johnny Kandinski, the copytaster, sitting at the head—he's *super*! He bought me a beer at lunch-time last Wednesday week ... All those rather dreary little men *not* in shirtsleeves at the table beyond Ropey are the reporters. They look as if they ought to have raincoats, don't they? ... Fancy! Look—here's that cosmetic firm copying the Ardette ads again. Trust the Americans! ... Those are the messengers over there: if you want one, you just shriek *Boy!* at the top of your voice—Oh, Donald, I'm awfully sorry! No, I didn't want anything: I was just sort of practising.

"... Look, what a scream! The dear old Foreign Secretary's at it again! A speech for women this time—here's the advance text. I suppose I'd better ring it just in case ... Where was I? Oh, yes—the smaller desks are for the specialist bits, you know, the picture desk, the art editor, the film people, the TV team and so on. The really grand ones live in these tiny offices partitioned off all round the room—the *writers* I mean, as distinct, you know, from the reporters ... Mr Warr's room is there—you know, the gossip man. He's a *dish*, but my dear, so *vieux jeu* . . . that surly old B who does the leaders is over there. And the nice one in the corner (it's got two windows, you know!) belongs to Luke Harold, the sports columnist—The Man They Daren't Keep Out. Actually, he's all right, really. Especially when he's drunk, which is about three minutes past noon every day . . ."

"Who's the lady I've got to see?" Emma asked when the girl drew breath.

" 'That's no lady, that's Marge Halloran,' she riposted, quick as a flash. 'Oh, Marge's okay. But there's always a bit of a battle on between her and Bronwen Heintz—she's the fashion editor, with a real office all to herself, down the passage with the editors and their deputies. Of course Beauty and Fashion are poles apart, separate pages on separate days and all that—but *technically* . . . technically, Marge is under Bronwen and neither of them can ever forget it . . ."

A few minutes later, Marjorie Halloran came in. She was wearing a lightweight grey suit with revers and lapels, from between which the frilled jabot of a crimson chiffon blouse projected. Her legs were as thin as a stork's and her heels were too high.

"Oh, yes, of course," she said when Emma introduced herself. "The lord telephoned me about you. We'll have a chat in a moment." She lit a cigarette with a gold-plated lighter. The fingers of her right hand were nicotine stained and the nails were chipped. Before she could begin again, a large woman in a flowered silk suit and an absurd hat materialised at the side of the desk. "Marjorie!" she crowed, hardly a crack appearing in her exquisitely painted face. "My dear, how I envy you! I can't tell you how much I'd give to be able to have my own little affairs in such apple-pie order that I could spare the time to stay at home until nearly twelve!"

"Bronwen you know perfectly well that I was at the opera reception last night—and it went on until three," the Beauty Editor said hotly, her cigarette wagging furiously between her lips.

"But, darling, of course. That's what I meant. And I do so applaud your courage in wearing something that *suits* you, instead of messing about with silly, feminine tulles and silks like the rest of us sheep."

"Those of us that actually have to *write* things for our living,

Bron darling, instead of just arranging for others to do it, find the drabber kind of clothes more practical in a newspaper office."

"So I see, Marjorie; so I see," the big woman said, moving away.

Marge Halloran was trembling with rage. Her expensively cut and expertly dressed hair bobbed up and down as she read her mail, muttering, shaking down a fine drain of dandruff on to the peppered shoulders of her suit. "I'm sorry," she said to Emma at last in a choked voice. "Now let's see what you can be doing . . ."

Five minutes later, Emma telephoned Steed's flat.

"Hallo?" His voice sounded vague, withdrawn.

"Steed? This is Emma Peel. I'm speaking from the *Courier*."

"Oh, so you got there all right. Splendid! How's it going?"

"Listen—there's a delicatessen near your flat, isn't there? Can you get something sent up for a cold lunch? Something's come up and I think I should see you to report in person."

"So you're going to spend your lunch hour—or, no, it's *two*, isn't it? —with me. How charming—" His voice suddenly broke off.

"Steed? Emma was a little jumpy. *"Steed?"*

Silence. Then clearly over the line she heard some kind of an explosion, the tinkling of shattered glass falling to the ground.

"Steed!" Her voice was urgent now. *"Steed are you all right?"*

Then, coolly, with a built-in chuckle, the exasperatingly calm voice drawling, "Hallo? Sorry about that, my dear! A slight detonation—a minor explosion. I left the percolating machine on too long—immersed in me work, you know! —and the heat evaporated so much water that atmospheric pressure had it's vile say and the glass thingummy caved in."

"You're not hurt?"

"Only in my *cuisinier's* pride—we Steeds are a race of men versed in the creation of gastronomic miracles, and a flop upsets us. There's a great deal of glass sticking into everything in the kitchen, but apart from that, there's no damage done."

"I wonder if you realise how exasperating you can be."

"Exasperating? Me? Why, I'm sure I don't know what—"

"I'll see you at one fifteen," Emma said. And put the phone down.

When she rang the bell under the little Georgian pediment

beside Steed's garage in Westminster Mews, it was a delivery boy who came down to open the front door for her. "He says you're to go up," the boy said, jerking his thumb over his shoulder. "Only use them stairs because the back ones are full of glass from the kitchen." He pushed past her and kick-started a large motor cycle leaning against the iron gates trellising the front of Steed's garage. Behind them, the doors were back and the Bentley looked down its aristocratic nose at the world.

Steed was surrounded by piles of old books and torn up leaves of paper. Beside him, as he squatted on the floor, a small mountain of packages wrapped in greaseproof paper rose. "Chicken, macedoine, potato salad, Greek rice, artichokes vinaigrettes," he intoned with a sweep of one arm. "There's a bottle of Chablis in the refrigerator. Plates in the rack. D'you think you could cope?—and mind the glass, do. I haven't had time to clear it up yet. Here—tear a page out of this will you?" He handed her up a dog-eared library edition of *Tales of Mystery and Imagination.*

"Tear a page out? Are you serious, Steed?"

"Yes, yes, yes. Tear a page out—tear it out as though there was some marvellous quote on it and you wanted to give it to me to keep for always."

"What page?"

"Good heavens, any page, woman! Just tear it out."

Emma looked at him for a moment, opened the book at random, took up a page in the forefinger and thumb of her right hand, holding it fairly near the spine, at the top, and tore it carefully along the line of the stitching.

She handed him the torn page with a puzzled expression.

"Thank you, Mrs Peel," Steed said drily. "Now do the same thing—no, don't put the book down!—do the same thing in a tearing hurry: as though it was equally important, but there wasn't a moment to lose; as if your life depended on doing it in no seconds flat."

Emma ripped another page from Poe. The tear started at the spine, but about half way down left the centre of the book and travelled in a diagonal direction towards the bottom right-hand corner. When she had finished, a triangle of paper remained attached to the book at its lower half.

"Splendid!" Steed exclaimed. "Now—one more time please! Would you please tear me out a page in a hurry, exactly as before, only this time bear in mind that the important bit, the bit you want to give me, is somewhere in the last dozen lines on the page, right?"

Emma thought a moment, then picked a page, holding it carefully *at the bottom* near the spine, between forefinger and thumb. She tore it rapidly upwards against the stitching—but after a short distance only, the tear again came away from the middle. Only this time it travelled diagonally *upwards*, towards the *top* right hand corner. The triangle of paper left in place was in fact the top part of the page . . .

"Thank you very much," Steed said. "That's most helpful. I got precisely the same results myself—and so did the boy from the delicatessen."

"Steed," Emma said, "I do have two hours for lunch. Even so—"

"My dear, I *am* so sorry," he said contritely, scrambling to his feet. "Here, let me help you lay the table . . ."

"I was not talking about food. Explanations are what I need!"

"Of course," Steed said. "Of course." While she cleared up the glass splinters and coffee grounds in the kitchen, he told her about finding the torn page in the dead man's hand. He moved on to his deliberations about the meaning or otherwise of the clue as she laid the table, detailing his researches—and their successful result—when she began to unwrap and lay out the food he had ordered.

"I think I can say pretty definitely that there's no vestige of a chance that there's any cryptographical meaning here," he said. "I've got a lot of pages of notebook to prove it! But that implies that any meaning there is must be implicit either in this particular page and the words on it, or in the *fact* that it comes from this particular book. If the latter—so what? The *fact* that Lindale happened to be consulting *Hemming's* tells me nothing. The book's too much in line with his normal work. Now if it had been a text book on orchid growing or a geological treatise . . . that would have been different! As it is, I'm going on the former assumption. And thus our little experiments. Will you do just one more for me, before we dissect the chicken?"

"Yes, of course," Emma said. "Now that I know what I'm doing . . "

"Right. Select a page—yes, that's it. Now *prepare* to tear it out *very* carefully . . ." As he spoke, Steed leaned forward and snatched the volume unexpectedly from her hand—rapidly and with some force. The leaf she was holding split about a third of its width out from the spine, leaving a jagged tear running the whole length of the the portion remaining, from top to bottom.

"There you are, you see!" Steed said delightedly. "That's the one test I couldn't do alone! And it confirms what I had thought. Look—the piece of paper I recovered from Lindale's hand is roughly triangular. There's the whole foot of the page, almost all of the outside margin, but only a dozen lines from the bottom of the margin nearest the spine. In other words, the tear goes from bottom left to top right . . . if it's the page 65 side you're looking at, that is."

"Yes, I see that," Emma said.

"Now we've seen from our own experiments that there's only one way a page'll tear like that. If you've got plenty of time, the whole leaf comes out properly anyway. If the book's torn out of your hand, there's a jagged tear all the way down. If you want the whole page, but you're in a frantic hurry, you get a diagonal tear—but with .the line going from top left to bottom right. *The only way you get the tear going from bottom left to top right is if you're tearing the page out upwards* . . . in other words, if the important part, the portion you want to preserve, the bit that holds the message, is at the foot of the page."

"D'you know," Emma said, "I'm almost inclined to rate that a good piece of deductive reasoning."

"When you've only got one clue, you examine it perhaps rather more carefully than you would if there were several," Steed said modestly. "Anyway, I think it's sufficiently logical for me to assume there *is* a message in that brief list of names I showed you. I shall proceed on that assumption—and in fact I've asked a friend of mine who's a particular genius on the subject of newspapers to call and see me about it later. In the meantime, there's nothing more I can do . . . So what's your news?"

"Just that Sir George Carew's making another speech.tonight. We have the advance text of it in the office."

"Is he. by Jove! And why does your department happen to have the advance text?"

"Because he's speaking at The Lady—you know, the exclusive female club in Curzon Street—and because his subject is,

naturally enough, a woman's one. I believe the actual title of
the lecture is *Woman And The Political Canvasser.*"

"You've seen the text?"

"Of course. It seems innocuous enough, I must say. He's
merely saying, if you're a political party organiser, and if you
particularly want to rope in the woman's vote, what's the best
way of going about it."

"It certainly sounds a theme unlikely to lend itself to distortion in the way we've come to know and love. But I'm convinced
that these people have to work quickly and at great pressure if
they're going to do anything. Concentration and intensity must
be their watchwords—so we have to expect them to use *any*
opportunity, however apparently unlikely."

"What do you suggest we do?"

"Can you go to the function at which he's speaking?"

"Not if I'm to hold down this job. The editor's sending me to
cover a simple press reception. It's being held to mark the opening of a new range of cosmetics. Nobody else wants to go—and
in fact it could perfectly well be written up from the handouts.
But apparently they advertise a lot in the *Courier* and the
powers-that-be feel it would be apreciated if somebody turns
up . . . even if the actual piece is written at the desk!"

"Where is it?"

"Well, actually, it's in Amsterdam, of all places!"

"But that's splendid!"

"I'm afraid I can hardly see why."

"Look—I'll go to the speech myself. I can fix it with the
gossip people: we're sure to have invitations. Then I'll go back
to the paper to keep an eye open. And of course I shall have
arranged a fairly elaborate system of surveillance—especially
around the furnaces and bits where they work on the matrices.
So any mischief-makers will be hard put to make their mischief.
You, on the other hand, will be in Holland—when do you go,
by the way?"

"The plane leaves about five this afternoon. The do is tonight
—and I have to be back at the office by lunchtime tomorrow."

"Good. Then you can stay in Amsterdam overnight—and
that means you can be on hand to witness the arrival of the
British papers tomorrow morning. If there's anything naughty
in them—and Holland has been one of the main targets so far—
you'll see it. And if none of us have seen anything, it'll give us

a better picture of where it's done, by a process of elimination. At least we should be able to narrow the field a little."

"If there *is* anything in them."

"Indeed. If there is. But I feel there might be," Steed said. "I say, you haven't had much chicken. Do let me carve you another wing?"

"Thank you," Emma said primly. "I have to work for my living—or so it seems now. I must be getting back."

"My goodness, yes," Steed said. "So must I. The gossip people start work at two thirty and continue (as they say) until unconscious. I'd better be on time my first day. Having spent the morning turning over, as it were, an old leaf, I'll have to spend the afternoon—"

"Steed!" Emma interrupted. "One of the few things I really like about you is that you *never* make puns! Don't finish that sentence."

"I'm sorry, my dear," the undercover man said with a smile. "One does work for a gossip column now, and one's sights, one supposes, have been correspondingly lowered. When in Rome, you know . . ."

"I know," Emma said tartly. "La Dolce Vita. Finish up your nice Chablis. Take off that prune thing, put on some clothes, and come with me."

7

MESSING WITH "THE MONSTROUS REGIMENT"!

THE man whose name graced the *Courier*'s gossip column each day was tall and thin, with a lock of dark hair perpetually falling over one eye. Bowing before the journalistic whims of Lord Borridale for more than 25 years had lined his face and honed a character already sharp with cynicism. But being one of "the lord's lads", as Borridale's personal favourites were dubbed in Fleet Street, had its compensations: at 45, Trewithick Polgadden-Warr could boast a sinecure, an easy and agreeable working life, and a generous pension to come later. His name had been made in the immediately pre-war years when his hair was longer and floppier—as were the society hostesses who liked their young men to look a little wayward. Since the days when it had been the means of his acquiring a series of sensational disclosures about the Sunday afternoon activities of the smart set, the iron grey had entered into his hair, and now he directed the column which bore his name from a small but comfortable office opening off the newsroom.

The staff who actually went out to the functions from which his copy was obtained were housed at a table just outside his door. They changed frequently and customarily differed in many respects from the other journalists on the paper—because the kind of stories required for "On The Warr Path" (as the column was still called) were inclined to lose the reporters who provided them friends. And because the kind of people who could get among those making gossip column news did not make normal newsmen.

When Steed reported for duty at two thirty, Warr himself was at the staff table talking to a dark girl in a beige twin-set and pearls, and two very young men—one fairish, pink-faced and clean; the other darkish, blue-jowled and not so clean.

"Polgadden-Warr, Trewithick," Steed said cheerily, hanging

his umbrella on a teleprinter. "I suppose you're not Cornish by any chance?"

"Good Lord, yes: I am as a matter of fact," Warr said. "How did you know?—Never mind. Let's get on with the day's briefings. There's three luncheons, a First Night, Carew's speech, press receptions at the Savoy and the Dorchester—and some French bird opening in cabaret at the Argosy. Any specials?" He looked over the top of his glasses at the journalists grouped around his desk.

"Yes, darling,"—it was the dark girl speaking—"Janet's at the Turkish lunch. She's arranged to have a word with the two belly dancers who're being brought in in the pie. It seems there has to be real juice in there, so the girls are to wear costumes in a kind of rubber called, believe it or not, chiffon latex!"

"God bless my soul!" Warr said, making a note on his pad.

"And apparently the story is that people in the Middle East like their belly dancers nice and puddingy and fat, and rubber garments make you sweat like the devil and get all slim—so they can't do the act very often. Or something like that."

"Pictures?"

"Oh, yes, naturally, darling. Ivor went down this morning and got them looking all shiny at rehearsal."

"Yes," Warr said with the resigned sigh of the man who knows all and sees all, "he would have. That's an obvious panel for Janet, anyway. Look No Belly, I suppose . . . Any more?"

"Charles said he'd been tipped off that waiters were going to demonstrate at the Greek dancers' reception tonight," one of the young men said. "That's why he's not here: he's staked out in the Savoy kitchens, waiting."

"Right. Could you contact him, David, and tell him we'll keep a couple of hundred words—but remind him to get the best quote from the dancers, eh? The lord likes to keep his boat in Piraeus most of the summer. You'll do the First Night afterwards, as usual?"

The young man nodded. "I looked in at the banking lunch," he said. "Nothing."

"As I thought. Nothing more? Oh, Vassily—you went to the picture dealers' lunch. Anything there?"

"Was nothing," the darker young man said mournfully. "Only a fat lady in silk trousers tell me she will stop some exhibition in Albemarle Street because her husband is not there. She looks like a madam but I do not understand—I thought all this kind of thing is stop, even in Albemarle Street."

"Good Lord!" Warr said. "That must have been the Marchioness of Witham—she always wears silk pants. I imagine she was referring to the New Advantage exhibition. She *can* stop it, too: she owns the lease of the building the gallery's in and she has a veto on anything they show. That must mean the selection committee's turned down Bennett's entry. Maureen —chase it up from both sides and get a firm quote from the old bag, will you, dear?"

"Okay. And you still want me to do the Dorchester after-wards?"

"Please. I think—er—I think I'll go out myself for a change tonight. I'll cover the cabaret at the Argosy. That just leaves the Carew speech. John—the lord particularly wants you to cover that. I suppose you have aunts there, or something. Give us a hundred words or so if anyone's *too* indiscreet will you, old boy?"

"More likely to stem from the uncles, if it's my family in-volved," Steed murmured. "I shall keep eyes *and* ears wide open . . ."

In the event, it was a precaution he need hardly have taken: it would have been difficult to avoid either manoeuvre, so strident was the baying of distaff voices, so bright the glitter of competing costume.

"So you're Polgadden-Warr, eh?" a strapping horsewoman who was acting as one of the reception committee boomed as she took Steed's card. "Thought you'd have been thinner, you know. Never mind. You've heard what Shaw called us, eh? The monstrous regiment of woman, eh, what! Well, tonight you're a guest in the officers' mess, ha, ha!"

"An honour that's greatly appreciated, believe me, Colonel," Steed said as he clapped her gently on one tweed shoulder and moved on up the stairs.

A buffet and drinks had been laid on before the Foreign Secretary's scheduled appearance. Through the tall, slim double doors of the reception hall at the top of the graceful staircase, he saw with trepidation the congested state of the party. Ninety per cent of the guests, naturally enough, were women. The few males present—most of them journalists or connected with the arts—preserved a discreet anonymity behind the façade of the dark suit and the white shirt. But the females thronging the panelled room rang a Treble Bob Major on the bells of change. From ball dresses to suits, from cocktail gowns to camping gear, they eddied and swayed in a kaleidoscope of leather and lace and worsted and chiffon and silk. Somewhat alarmed, Steed edged his way in and accepted a large pink gin from a large pink waitress with a tray. Once secure behind the rim of his glass, he turned slowly from side to side like a radar scanner, drinking in whatever his ears could catch.

". . . well, *really,* Edith, I should have thought you'd have known better than to listen to tittle-tattle like that," a gorgeous creature in black velvet was saying on his left "What *exactly* did she say . . .?"

". . . only fifteen and eleven a yard," a birdlike lady in horn rims was advising on the other side. "And of course you don't need to interline them if the window faces an air-shaft . . ."

". . . when she walked into shot, you could still see the whole left side of her face positively *working,* you know . . ."

". . . unexpected pleasure for me to be among all these ladies, ha, ha—but I wonder if I could ask you girls if you've heard this little story?"

Steed moved on. A few paces nearer the white-clothed bar, a girl of about thirty with big breasts, a pouting mouth and a faint moustache was holding forth to a circle of friends in low-cut print dresses. ". . . so the hotel-keeper said, *oui, mademoiselle,* but we have only the two rooms with one double bed in each. Well you can imagine how we all felt!"

"Oh, Sally!" they all chorused. "What did you *do?*"

"Well, I'm sure he must have thought we were all completely *mad,* but we decided that the boys would take . . ."

Steed raised an eyebrow and sauntered on. Perhaps he would hear something a little less trivial from one of the few groups of males present. Here was a knot of elegantly turned-out men in this corner. He accepted another drink from a waitress even more starched than the first.

". . . couldn't tell if he was *omi-palone* or not until he used the fingerbowl. But after seeing those *expressive* hands, of course . . ."

". . . in flounced madam, camping herself *silly.* She might as well have put on the full drag and have done with it, really!"

"But, goodness me, what did Charles say?"

"*Charles?* She was at her wits' *end*, of course. But positively *green*. Still, dear, you know how it is with these robust ones . . ."

Steed raised the other eyebrow and wedged himself in among the press around the bar. None of this banality seemed to be likely to lead to any distortion of what Sir George Carew was likely to say, or any perversion—at least of his speech. He leaned against the wall and fixed his gaze on the sham renaissance ceiling, allowing the tide of conversation from every side to submerge him. Perhaps there might be something . . .

". . . oh, mustn't complain, old boy. Mustn't complain. One presses on, you know."

"Regardless, Dick? Or have the *Gazette* equipped you with that indispensable adjunct to the successful critic, the social conscience? . . ."

". . . or would madam prefer whisky, perhaps? Certainly, miss. I'm coming now . . . Yes, sir. Yes . . ."

". . . there was this Yiddisher fellow, see—this'll amuse you girls in the dress trade, I'm sure!—this Yiddisher fellow says, You ask me How is my wife and How is my daughter, he says; but you don't ask me, How is business? . . ."

". . . liked your piece on Gloria de Guy, darling. Very naughty!"

"Well, thank God at least somebody reads me still!"

"Cheers, darling . . . I do hope you don't mind my mentioning it, but that hat . . ."

". . . two champagne cocktails, please, Meriel. And a large gin . . ."

". . . out in the garden, I suppose. You know Oscar! A little heat wave means nothing to Oscar when there's a calceolaria at stake—Oh! Did you hear that! I said a calceolaria *at stake* . . ."

". . . so this other fellow says, Well, he says, How *is* business then? And the Yiddisher fellow says, *Business?* he says. Oh, he says, don't *ask*! . . ."

". . . not too much time while the bundles are in the vans on their way to London Airport, because the new front pages . . ."

Steed jerked upright off the wall, every sense at the alert. *Who was it that had made that last remark?* A woman, her voice anonymous among the hundreds of others. Nothing, no accent, no intonation, no depth or timbre to distinguish it from the dozens of similar voices chattering within earshot. He looked along the length of the bar. It could have been any of them. The voice would not have come amiss from any of the faces drinking, laughing, talking, giggling, sneering there. Would he even know it if he heard it again? He began to move along the bar, threading his way slowly from group to group. But it was too late. On the other side of the reception hall, a severe looking woman in a black dress with white collar and cuffs was banging a billiard cue on the floor.

"Ladies," she boomed. "Ladies and gentlemen. Sir George Carew will be addressing the meeting in a very few minutes. The bar is now closed—until after the speech, of course, when it will be open again. Now, if you'd kindly file into the lecture room through the door at *this* end of the hall . . ."

The Foreign Secretary was red-faced and bristling of moustache, with a shining scalp surmounting a fringe of dark hair. Above the network of veins mottling each cheek, the eyes, pale blue and protuberant, lent him that expression at once outraged and incredulous that was the especial delight of the political cartoonists. His speech, as both Emma and Polgadden-Warr had foreseen, was dull and predictable. It was a steady, methodical examination of the means statistically proved to be the most successful in the wooing of women's votes. As delivered, nobody could conceivably take offence at it, Steed thought. And there wasn't a foreign country mentioned.

The club's P.R. woman tracked him down when it was over —five foot five inches of carefully rehearsed personality in a flowered silk cocktail suit—and backed him up against a wall in the bar. "So *you're* the Warr to end all wars!" she said. "Somehow I'd pictured you a little different, you know—a little more careworn, a little more frail. Perhaps even a little more *vapid* . . . I do hope you don't mind—"

"Be my guest," Steed said good-humouredly. "After all, it's only the superficial qualities that last: one's deeper nature is soon found out."

"Oh, jolly good!" the girl said. "That's Oscar Wilde isn't it?"

"It has to be admitted. One can improvise freely on the theme, however."

"For instance?"

"Oh—that the cheap papers fool the public, but the serious ones fool themselves . . . Or that bad journalists are jealous of their reputations, but good journalists never have enough time for this. They are too busy being jealous of other people's reputations."

The girl clapped her hands with pleasure. "Splendid!" she crowed. "You could almost make a living doing that, I should say!"

"You could *almost* make a living doing any kind of journalism," Steed replied, getting into the spirit of the thing.

"Yes, I suppose—Oh, Lady B! How nice. May I present Mr Polgadden-Warr of the *Courier*? Mr Warr, this is Lady Brownlow . . ."

"But I know Simon Warr. You don't resemble him in the slightest," a thin blonde with flared nostrils objected, taking his hand dubiously. She was wearing a dress made in Paris that—as befitted a prominent society hostess—revealed hardly any of the artistry that had gone into its manufacture but a great deal of Lady Brownlow herself.

"Enchanted," Steed intoned, bending over her hand. "I don't actually admit to being an impostor, though. My name is Steed —John Steed. Warr has to have help with his column, you know: today alone, he would have been obliged to consume three luncheons, two dinners and a quantity of food and drink at four or five other functions throughout the evening, had he in fact covered them all himself. It's all printed under his name, however."

"So he gets the kudos for your work?"

"And the blame, if we make a mistake."

"Yes, I see. How fascinating. Tell me, Mr Steed, are you a leg man, then?"

"What good features man isn't?" he replied obliquely, lowering his eyes and disengaging his fingers from the cool, dry pressure of Lady Brownlow's hand.

The P.R. girl was coming to the rescue. "Oh, Mr—Steed, isn't it? Mr Steed you *must* meet Mrs Lestrade-Gordon . . ."

Steed found himself held at bay by an aggressively nubile woman of about forty who had packed herself into gold cocktail trousers and a truly remarkable top. She had a hoarse, ginny voice and wore too much make-up. "Always delighted to meet another newspaper face," she said. "But I was just saying to Liz Macrae of the *Gazette* how they're all changing—the faces, I mean. One hardly recognises a soul now."

"It's not so much the faces, you know. The faces remain the same—it's the people behind them who change. And there are no souls left to recognise."

"Yes, I daresay there's something in that. But I mean you only have to look . . . they're all *altering*. For the worse if you ask me!"

"Perhaps we attend too many nice parties at ladies' clubs— er, thank you, my dear. Yes, a little tonic with it, if you please."

"Pretty gel," Mrs Lestrade-Gordon observed, staring approvingly after the departing waitress. "What were you saying?— Oh, yes. Do you go to many parties, Mr Steed? You must come to one of ours . . . *Marianna!* Here a moment, darling . . . Mr Steed, I'd like you to meet Marianna. I was telling Mr Steed here, darling, that he must come to one of our parties."

Marianna was strikingly beautiful—very dark, with thin, proudly curling lips and smudged eyes. She must have been all of twenty-two. "Not a bad pair of shoulders on him," she said, looking critically at Steed. "Yes, darling, let's have him along."

"Isn't she lovely?" the older woman said fondly. "Oh, Hilary darling—meet Mr Steed . . ." She dragged forward a short-haired woman built like a wing forward and pushed her in front of Steed. The undercover man made the right noises, moving tactfully from group to group, listening, always listening; hoping to hear again and identify the voice he had heard for so tantalisingly short a time before the speech.

Finally, he tracked down Carew himself in a small ante-room, introducing himself while the Foreign Secretary's hostess was away fetching a fresh drink.

"Steed?" he said. "Oh, yes, they told me you'd probably be here. Well—see anything suspicious, what? See any chaps with whiskers whose shirt fronts light up with the word Anarchist, ha, ha?"

"Not exactly. I did hear a stray phrase tossed up among a great sea of conversation, though—something about time and airports and new front pages. Unfortunately, I couldn't see who it was that made the remark, nor to whom it was addressed— so I'm spending the rest of the party toddling around with both ears flapping, hoping I'll hear it again."

Carew shook his head decisively. "Wasting your time, my boy," he said. "Take my word for it, what you heard was just a coincidence—your mind's filled with all this balderdash the security people have been talking so naturally it's ready to supply sinister meanings to anything a little out of the ordinary that you hear."

"There may be something in that. But after all, Sir George, there *have* been fake stories misquoting you on the Continent. *Somebody* must be doing it, mustn't they?"

"They must indeed. But the operative word in what you just said was 'Continent'. I don't mind telling you—"

"But I thought it was fairly well established—excuse me for interrupting you—I thought it was fairly well established that the forgeries could simply not, physically, be done on the Continent?"

"Not a bit of it. You take my word for it, Peel. That's where the damage is done."

"Steed, sir, actually. But I mean there are actual, tangible difficulties, reasons why it could not be done over there—"

"Nonsense. They're a slippery lot, your continentals. You may depend on it, Steel, they wangle it somehow or other. Stands to reason. I mean, it's not the sort of thing you'd find a chap *doing* over here, now is it, I ask you?"

"As long as I do find the chap, it doesn't matter too much to me where I find him," Steed said. "And such information as I have leads me to suppose that the fixture's more likely to be a Home than an Away one."

The Foreign Secretary wagged a reproving finger. "Come, come, my dear fellow," he said. "Let's not have any of that bolshie stuff here. There are ladies present, what! Of course *I* understand that you were joking, but others might not—and these are serious matters, hey? You take it from me, young man —and believe me I *know* these people—you take it from me: as soon as you begin looking on the other side of the Channel, that's when you'll begin to strike oil. What did you say your name was?"

"Steed, Sir George," the undercover man said, with a resigned sigh. "Anyway, I expect we shall be crossing the Channel soon. There's a colleague of mine in Amsterdam now, as it happens."

"There you are then. You do as I say, and you'll get results. You won't regret it—Ah! Here's Eleanor back with me drink. Splendid!" He accepted a champagne cocktail from the horsey woman in tweeds and flat shoes who had greeted Steed when he came in. "Eleanor," he said with a vague sweep of his arm, "I don't believe that you'll have met Mr Peak from—ah—let's just say—ah—the Foreign Office, shall we?"

"But George, you old fool," the lady cried before he could complete the introduction, "you've got the names all wrong as usual! That's not Mr *Peak*! I met him when he came in: that's Mr Warr . . ."

Thankfully, Steed beat a strategic retreat and picked his way downstairs to retrieve his umbrella and hat. As he went, the tide of conversation surged about him as before—such pieces of verbal flotsam as bumped against him now differing from their predecessors only in being a little more sodden, a trifle less crisp . . .

". . . back to my place for a spot of . . . then on to the Tiara. They have a—have a—sort of a—in the basement. Attractive woman like you must dance, eh? Can't keep my hands . . ."

". . . do hope Esmeralda's all *right*: she's been in there an hour . . ."

". . . no, darling, I mean it, I mean it. Really I do. Yes, really . . ."

". . . no, I *must* tell you. There's this little man . . ."

". . . a pleasure, madam. Thank *you*, I'm sure. Very generous . . ."

". . . *Steed*! Mr Steed! Just a moment; I wanted to ask whether you'd possibly be able to come to a little luncheon party I'm having in Park Street next Thursday—Oh, you can't? Have you really? What a bore for you, dear! Marianna will be so disappointed . . ."

". . . has anyone for God's sake seen Charles? . . ."

". . . Don't cry, my dear. Men can be brutes, can't they? Why don't you come up to my room—yes! I live here!—come up to my room and *relax* while I get the porter to bring us up a nice cup of tea . . ."

". . . No, sorry, I got it wrong: the *agent* says, What do you call the act? And the *husband* says, Call it? he says; why we call it The Four Sophisticates, he says . . ."

". . . Charles! . . ."

". . . I'm through, d'you hear? As far as I'm concerned, you can walk the whole way back . . ."

". . . and when they'd got their clothes off . . ."

". . . *Charles*! . . ."

". . . can't. I simply can't, that's all. My coat . . ."

". . . for the life of me see what he saw, why he saw—why you sexy thing, you. I want to put . . ."

"Yes, sir. A bowler with a curly brim and an umbrella, wasn't it?"

The bulky woman with straw-coloured hair bustled about behind the cloakroom counter. At first, she brought Steed the wrong umbrella. As he was leaning over the much-polished wood, trying to point out to her where his own was hanging, he caught sight of a familiar profile among the rows of coats and hats on the pegs in a small room to one side of the counter. It was Sandra Gillan, Robin Creighton's secretary from the *Courier*. At first she tried to move back quickly out of his range of vision. But Steed called out, "Hallo, there! Fancy seeing you!"—and the girl, looking as supercharged as ever in a soft, white leather dress draped provocatively over her chest, came reluctantly out towards the counter.

"Oh, good evening. Mr Steed, isn't it?" she asked in her aloof voice. "This is your first assignment, I suppose?"

"For the *Courier*," Steed—who had been taught not to lie as a child—corrected her.

"Of course. I wasn't so naïve as to imagine that you were entirely without experience."

"I'm relieved to hear that. It might be a dangerous mistake to make, Miss Gillan—especially after an evening wine-bibbing *chez les girls*! May I drop you anywhere? I'm off back to the office to write my piece."

"No thank you. I've promised to relieve my friend here. She has a—er—date. Hilde," she added, turning her back deliberately, yet not rudely, on Steed, "don't you think you ought to be making tracks?"

The bulky woman nodded, pressed Sandra Gillan's arm above the elbow, and left the cloakroom through another door. "And the next, please?" the blonde girl chanted. "One-o-seven—thank you, sir. A brief case only, is it? Here we are, then . . . Yes, madam. Lost your ticket have you? Perhaps if you could describe the coat . . ."

Steed settled his hat at its evening angle and left.

On the steps outside several groups of people remained chatting—rather like a Sunday congregation on their way home to lunch from church. The air was sultry and heavy. The heat, instead of being dissipated by the evening air, seemed to have

been sucked up and stored by the dark so that now, at every
point where street-lamp, window, awning or neon pierced the
night, it leaked out and drenched everything in sight with its
humid embrace. A chauffeur in one of the large cars waiting
outside the club had turned his radio on. Clearly on the stifling
air the voice of the announcer floated, saying: ". . . for all
shipping. Here is a Gale Warning . . ."

"Good grief!" Steed muttered loudly. "Surely not! No, it
couldn't be . . ."

"What is it, Mr Steed?" a merry voice at his ear enquired.
"Have you forgotten something, then?" It was the P.R. girl,
completing her duties by seeing the invited off the premises.

"No, no, thank you," Steed said vaguely. "Remembered
something would be nearer the mark. Something I heard on the
radio reminded me for a moment of someone I used to know . . .
a former colleague, say . . ."

"Did you think you saw him here?"

"No indeed. She—it was a female colleague—is to the best
of my knowledge on an anthropological expedition to
Guatemala."

"Well, we get all sorts—but it seems on the face of it unlikely
in this case. Which leaves me only my exit line to say. Bearing
in mind the main entertainment of the past few hours, one might
return to our previous game to note that only the masters of
style ever succeed in being really obscure! Or, better still, perhaps—that only the speakers with nothing to say, ever succeed
in saying it really well!" She waved him Goodnight and
scrambled back up the steps to the foyer. Steed laughed—then
saw beyond her plump and friendly back the dread features of
Lady Brownlow, remorselessly bearing down like a blonde and
full-rigged ship upon the steps.

He turned and fled.

In the *Courier* building, the air-conditioning rendered the heat
more breathable, but there was the same tension all around, the
same powder-keg-waiting-for-a-match atmosphere to unsettle
the unwary. Warr was sitting at his desk with his spectacles on,
altering the layout of his column for the later editions with the
help of a young sub. "We'll have to take in a couple of pars
from Maureen," he said. "Plus the waiters' demonstration, plus
John's bit on the bulls at play—Oh, John, dear boy! How were
those ghastly butch creatures, then? Did the man with the

boiled-sweet eyes say anything indiscreet? Were there any signs of fakery? And, last but not least, what are you going to write for us?"

"Answers in order," Steed said in the same tone of voice. "One—ghastly. Two—not during his speech. Three—all over the shop, but not of the kind you mean. Four and last—rather a nice little quote, I think, recalling that old remark of Bernard Shaw's about the monstrous regiment—"

"And you being a guest at the officers' mess. I know. Good God, don't say Eleanor Tigham's at it again," Warr said in exasperation.

"That *was* her name, actually," Steed said in some perplexity. "But I'm afraid that I don't quite understand. How did you know? And how on earth could you have known what she said . . ?"

"Simply because the old cow's made the same remark at every do the Cattery's put on for the last fifteen years," the columnist said wearily. "It's her stock in trade—the one semi-original thought she ever had, I suppose—and she cannot resist plugging it. And every time we send a new bod there, he or she falls for it. What else?"

"A scholarly little paragraph involving some rather neat paraphrases of Wilde's *Phrases And Philosophies For The Use Of The Young,* involving the club's P. R. lady, whose name—"

"Too egghead for us. And P.R. people do not exist. The lord refuses to recognise them. Our stories always come through our own industry, never through a handout. As I sat next to him at lunch, he told me—that's our line on press releases. And?"

"Lady Brownlow says—"

"Sorry old boy. She'll be in the *Globe.* Probably the *Gazette,* too. We can't afford to double on her."

"Well, there's a woman called Lestrade-Gordon—"

"And that gorgeous zombie she hires out? I know. Have you ever been thrashed, Steed?"

"I beg your pardon? Not since I took the housemaster's daughter to the flicks, I don't think. Why?"

"You would have been, probably, if you'd accepted their invitation! No, they're much too hot to handle—they're the pair who were up before that Breach of Privilege tribunal last month, remember? Did you see Carew?"

"Oh, yes. We had a bit of a chat, you know."

"Splendid. Give us a hundred on him then."

After Steed had typed out a mendacious report chronicling how the Foreign Secretary had confided in him that he only drank champagne cocktails because the cognac in them was likely to have been distilled by a British-owned firm, he went back to Warr's office and handed in the sheet of typescript. "Splendid," the columnist said, glancing cursorily at the wordage. "We'll get it in the re-hash Ted and I are dressing up for the two-star. The waiters' demo turned out to be such good copy that the news boys took it over and left us with a hole to fill."

"Have the news people done anything with Carew's speech itself?"

"Good lord, no. That was chucked out as soon as they saw the advance. Nothing in it—unless he ad-libbed, that is . . . He did keep to the text, I suppose?"

"One could almost say religiously."

"That's all right then. Here—I must get on: I've got to get across to that blasted club for whatsername's opening, or we shall have no lead for tomorrow . . ."

"I don't suppose any of the other papers will be running anything on the speech, will they?" Steed asked.

Warr stared at him. "I should be most surprised if they did," he said. "Who'd want to know his views—anyone's views for that matter—on how to ingratiate yourself with a lady voter! Why do you ask?"

"Just wondered," Steed said vaguely. "That's what *I* thought. So I wondered why he bothered to make a speech at all . . ."

"To ingratiate himself with lady voters, of course," the sub called Ted remarked as they turned back to their lay-out sheets.

Steed drifted back through the newsroom. Most of the features desks at Warr's end of the place were in shadow, the lights out, the chairs pushed in and the typewriters covered. But there was a pandemonium of activity centred on the sub-editor's table, the fierce strip lighting cascading down on men in shirt-sleeves busily typing, casting up copy or headlines with their type scales, or scribbling with a ballpoint on huge lay-out sheets. Small islands of light surrounded this bright centre to the huge room: a bald man in glasses furiously marked up photographs at the picture desk; two or three reporters pored over notebooks at their own table; the night editor was engaged in an argument with a photographer, festooned with his equipment like the

White Knight. And over it all hammered the incessant noise of the newspaper—teleprinters clattering, bells shrilling, typewriters clicking, voices calling and messengers running, punctuated every now and then by the hiss and thump of the pneumatic tube fetching and carrying copy and proofs between the newsroom and the printshop upstairs.

The undercover man faded gently from the scene. If no newspapers were running any of Carew's speech at all, then it seemed unlikely that any attempt would be made to disseminate a bogus one on the Continent—all the previous forgeries had been effected on the occasion of an actual speech which had been reported, however briefly. In addition, the previous speeches had all been made either at luncheons or early in the afternoon, and had thus comfortably got in to the early editions of the papers. Tonight's effort, had anybody bothered to carry any of it, had been made too late to catch anything before the editions printed around midnight—and therefore too late to appear in the editions to be sold tomorrow on the Continent.

Nevertheless, arrangements had been made. Steed had spoken at length on the telephone that afternoon with the result that, had the *Courier*'s personnel manager chanced to visit the building that evening, he would have been surprised to see a number of unfamiliar faces in key positions. Certain workers had sent in fully qualified deputies, it seemed, and in other places there appeared to be supernumeraries in evidence . . . Oddly enough, exactly the same thing had happened at the offices of the *Globe* and the *Gazette*.

From these infiltratees, as he called them, Steed now had to extract verbal reports of what had, or had not, occurred that evening during the printing of the early editions of the papers concerned.

He went upstairs to the stone, exchanged a few words with a deputy press-man, strolled past the furnaces and stopped under the *No Smoking* sign to offer a cigarette to one of the men making-ready a matrix near the forme-lift, and then went down the stairs to the machine room and out via the loading bay. He seemed to have made quite a few acquaintances in the short time he had been there. A man in a boiler suit asked him for a light on the stairs and then paused to pass the time of day. He was greeted by another amid the roar of machinery and handed a tip for the next day's first race in a small envelope. And the driver of the articulated lorry backed into the loading bay to get rid of its huge paper rolls greeted him like a brother. After the furious blare of heat among the presses, the still night air seemed almost refreshing, and Steed stayed chatting with him for some minutes before walking through into Fleet Street for a rendezvous at the dairy with a man from the *Globe*. Later he walked on to Farringdon Road and had a drink with two or three friends in a pub at the side of the *Gazette* building.

And by the time he raised his umbrella to hail a cab to ferry him to a late dinner in St. James's, he knew positively and definitely that there had been no forgeries among any of the bundles of newspapers leaving the Street for the Continent *that* evening . . .

8

EMMA'S DUTCH TREAT

THE extraordinary thing was that there *were* forgeries among the British papers by the time they were on sale in continental cities—only in one paper, the *Courier,* this time; but in some ways probably the most virulent yet to appear. And almost as soon as Emma Peel found out about it in Amsterdam, someone tried to murder her.

She had had an agreeable assignment the day before. Journalists arriving at Schipol airport had been met and taken to Amsterdam, entertained very well while the new range of cosmetics was unveiled and introduced, and dined and wined extravagantly at the *rijstafel* on the lower floor of the Dutch capital's canal-side restaurant, the Lido. Back at the comfortable, old-fashioned hotel near the Rembrandtsplein, Emma sat in one of seven armchairs with which her enormous bedroom was equipped and looked across acres of sombre red carpet at a wardrobe in very dark wood which resembled—both in size as well as in design—a small gothic cathedral. The sheer incongruity of the place, especially in contrast to her own streamlined apartment in London, prompted her to make certain modifications to two of the cosmetic company's gimmicks which had especially pleased her: a lipstick and case which incorporated a tiny atomiser, spraying out a fine cloud of toilet water or scent if one squeezed the ends together; and a peculiarly thin compact with a very strong lid which could be used "puffer"-style to make an even distribution of fine powder.

She rose very early and made her way across the matchless confusion of Amsterdam's street plan to Paulus Potterstraat, where the small, modern, beautifully arranged Stedelijk Museum housed a Mondrian, a Van Gogh and several impressionist paintings of which she wanted to refresh her memory. The sun was bright but pale, the air crisp, with none of the heavy, thunderous overtones spoiling the sky of London. A light wind ruffled the surface of the canals and fragmented the reflections of the ancient, rose coloured houses with their sandstone copings and steeply tiled roofs.

After she had seen what she wanted to see at the museum, she carried her overnight bag across the incredible green grass of the square to the one-storey KLM terminal. One of the hourly buses to Schipol would be leaving in twenty minutes, she was told. She checked in her case and spent the time on crisp rolls and the best coffee in Europe: there was a roll shop, a "Broodje van Kootje", not far away in the Leidseplein.

The airport at Copenhagen could be nowhere but in Denmark. In their dusty, faintly seedy way, the passport and customs sections of Orly and Le Bourget could house nothing but French bureaucracy. Even the brave show achieved at Heath Row dwindles to a British dreariness immediately the traveller sees the closed restaurants or lets his eye fall on the dreadful food at the snack bars. But, so much closer have the aircraft themselves brought us, the majority of continental airports now have a sort of cosmopolitan universality of style. Rome, Nice, Stockholm, Brussels, Geneva—even Tempelhof, Berlin, and the little ones like Southend or Caselle at Turin—each of them is practically indistinguishable from the others. And Schipol, just outside Amsterdam, rests firmly in this second category.

Cigar smoke predominates, perhaps, just a little in the overheated air of the departure lounges, pushing the aromas of coffee, strong cigarettes and spirits that much further into the background. The majority of men sitting waiting on the green imitation leather seats may be a trifle more solid and dependable, a little less raffish than the normal cross-section of air travellers; but the *atmosphere* of the place, the way the buildings fan out singly from the control tower and then proliferate when they're out of sight of the entrance hall; the clean lines of cars parked by special signs: the leaning sightseers on the observation terraces; the hustle and bustle in the hall itself—these could be anywhere in Europe.

Emma made friends with a smooth-haired young officer from Traffic Control. Over *Steinhagger* and *pils* at the bar, she confided her wants to him and he obligingly brought across a friend from the passport section and another who worked in the press office. As soon as she produced her press card and mentioned that she would like to see the airport from the operating side—

especially the freight section—the three young men announced
themselves as only too eager to help. Writing a feature on the
advantages of air transport, was she? Well, she couldn't find a
better model than Schipol . . . Over a hundred aircraft a day
landed and took off for cities in 60 countries—but it was still
small enough for one to get an *overall* picture, unlike London
or Paris, the young man from the press office said with pride.

It was the nerve centre of the helicopter shuttle service
between the northern European capitals, the Traffic Control boy
added. When it was built from the bed of a reclaimed lake in
1920, it covered 76 hectares; now it was more than ten times
that size—and in the same period the number of passengers
carried per year had risen from 440 to a million . . .

"Thank you, thank you!" Emma interrupted, laughing.
"That's all frightfully interesting—but I'm not going to write
a handbook on the place: I'd just appreciate a glimpse behind
the scenes, as it were. If I could possibly just wander about—I
wouldn't get in anyone's way, I promise—out between the
lounges and the aircraft themselves, that would be marvellous.
Do you think it could be managed without too much trouble?"

"But of course," the young man from Passport Control said
in his soft-spoken, swallowed English. "Höwelbroek will let you
through. I will speak with him now."

He hurried off, to return a few minutes later, smiling and
nodding. The four of them passed through a doorway, marked
Private in four languages, under the benign gaze of a large,
close-cropped man sitting at a high-legged desk. Beyond, Emma
found herself in a long passage leading directly to the apron.

"Here you shall be finding airplanes from thirteen foreign
companies beside our own KLM," the young man from Traffic
Control told her. "Now must I return to my work, and so I
left you with our friends."

Emma walked out into the sunshine, hotter now but still fresh
and dry, with the remaining two officials. Aircraft lay about the
huge concrete park like stranded fish. Above and behind them,
long rows of faces lined the observation terrace like those of
passengers on a departing liner—only this time it was the passengers who stayed behind, and the people on the ground below
who were going away . . . They walked across the apron, past
a flight of passengers being led, sheeplike, to a plane by a trim
young Lufthansa stewardess. Out on what had become at this

level the horizon of the flat field, a Trident touched down half way along the immense main runway. Nearer at hand, a jet engine coughed twice and then broke into full song somewhere behind a row of small twin-engined planes carrying the KLM "Flying Dutchman" insignia.

"This is the maintenance area we are coming to, now," the man from the passport section told her. "You will excuse me, but I have to go on here. Please—you will return through the door we came from? I am being responsible for this, as he has allowed you without a passport through."

"Of course I will," Emma said warmly, flashing him a brilliant smile "And thank you *very* much for your help . . ."

She persuaded her friend from the press office to take her over the freight arrival section and she was just about to ask him where and how the newspapers from England came in when there was an incomprehensible gargling noise from the P.A. system loudspeakers, expanding and echoing unintelligibly among the roof trusses of the huge hangar they were in.

The young man stopped in mid-stride, laying a hard hand on her arm. "Please," he said. "They call me on the radio, you know. I must go to my office—you shall be okay waiting here, then?"

"Yes, of course. Off you go. I shall be quite happy here. I'll browse around and look about—and then I'll wait for you to come back," Emma said, relieved at the good chance that was to leave her alone where she had wanted to be left.

"Very good then," the young man said. "Go where you want —but, please, not to smoke on apron . . . and take care from the exhowst from the jat engine!"

Once alone, Emma moved apparently at random but in fact in a planned "quartering" of the great building. After a few minutes, she came across a hand trolley loaded with square bundles of newspapers, wrapped in newsprint and tied with string, which had obviously been left conveniently near the doors for early collection. Beyond it were two more.

She prowled around the trolleys examining the bundles. Most of them were wrapped in copies of papers printed the previous day. She identified *Gazettes, Globes, Suns, Mirrors* and *Mails* among these. Another journal remained in discreet anonymity behind inpenetrable paper in plain brown. The *Courier* alone— which she found had a trolley all to itself, although the bundles did not fill it—was wrapped in the same day's papers.

And as soon as she set eyes on the main story on the front page, Emma gasped and dragged a pencil and notebook from her handbag, copying down the coded letters and figures of instruction and address on the wrappings.

There were several people busied about various piles of merchandise in the vicinity. The jet engines that were being warmed up outside rose to a scream, stirring the dust and pieces of paper lying in the open doors of the hangar. A porter chugged past on an electric trolley, drawing a long string of small-wheeled trucks behind.

Emma acted boldly and swiftly. She took one stride to the *Courier* trolley, sawed through the string with the blade of a penknife, and quickly abstracted two of the front pages which were tucked in the flap of the wrappings almost as though they were samples of what lay within. She glanced around. Nobody seemed to have noticed anything. Removing the rest of the cut string and rolling it into a ball which she stuffed into her pocket, she moved casually to the hangar doors and went outside.

While she leaned her elegant back—clothed today in a light-weight cinnamon suit, its jacket frogged with white p.v.c.—against the metal wall, waiting for her obliging escort to return, she unfolded one of the pages and looked at it more closely.

It looked a typical first edition lead—the sort of story editors put in when they know very well that something important is likely to break (or hope to God that something important will break!) before the second. A PAT ON THE BACK FOR MISS ENGLAND! the banner proclaimed. And underneath, there was printed: *Foreign Secretary criticises foreign secretaries.*

Miss England today can give herself a hearty pat on the back—she's more intelligent, more attractive, more faithful, more fun, a better wife . . . and *cleaner* than her continental sisters! That was the message Sir George Carew, the Foreign Secretary, had for an exclusive women's club in London's West End yesterday.

"You don't want to believe any of these stories put about that continental women are better managers, better companions, better housewives—or for that matter better anything—than you are," Sir George told members of the The Lady at a reception to mark the club's 25th Anniversary.

"Believe me," he added, "I've been to these places: my job takes me there—and some times I wish it didn't . . .

"Take this question of cleanliness," Sir George Carew continued. "Now everyone is brought up to believe that the Dutch are the cleanest nation in Europe—neat, colourful little gardens, spotless interiors, and so on. In fact the average Dutch housewife is a slattern, her living room a chaos of poor planning—and her kitchen and bathroom haunts of lurking disease."

Emma read on for a few paragraphs and then shivered. She stuffed the pages of newsprint into the waistband of her skirt. It was diabolically clever. Nothing could have been better designed to enrage the Dutch, traditionally the most pro-British nation in Europe since the 1939-45 war, than this totally unwarranted attack, which was as unjustified as it was unfair, on their pride. She felt embarrassed at being associated, however indirectly, with the forgery—and she hoped that her plane would have left before the papers had been put on sale.

For a moment, she toyed with the idea of trying to get publication of the offending journal stopped. But a moment's thought brought home the futility of that course—even if she could succeed in having it taken. Similar forgeries were no doubt about to be put on sale in Rome and Paris and other capitals. What good would it do to suppress one load in these circumstances, when the same lies were about to be published all over Europe?

She was relieved when her young man from the press office returned to conduct her back inside the airport buildings. So far, he had not seen the offending edition, so she was able to thank him for his courtesy with a clear mind. It would have been most awkward had he seen the paper, since Emma was accepting favours from him as a staff member of the very organ publishing the lies . . .

Feeling an uncleanliness that was almost physical, she pushed open the flush-fitting door of the ladies' cloakroom and went in to wash her hands. She found that the row of washbasins, with their towels, soap, brushes and *eau de Cologne*, was empty. The attendant seemed to have slipped out for a moment or two.

Emma took off rings, watch and bracelet, placing them on the cool porcelain surround to the basin as she ran the water and prepared to refresh herself for the journey. The basin was deep and she allowed it almost to fill before plunging her arms in up to the elbow. She leaned down to splash water on her face.

It was while she was groping blindly for a towel, a fragment of soap having got into her eye, that the attack occurred.

She never knew what it was that made her look into the

mirror over the basin just at that moment. One eye was screwed shut against the smart of the soap, her hair was drenched, and she needed the other eye to look for something to bathe out the soap with. Perhaps in fact there was a noise. Whatever the reason, she did look—and went suddenly cold to the soles of her feet.

An apparition, a monster stood there—about six feet tall and nearly as broad, it looked at first. The arms, the obscene, bulky body, the head were all covered in gleaming yellow: a heavy plastic that creaked rubberily and flashed highlights about its moving surfaces as it advanced. But the awful thing about it was that it had no face. The shining stuff covered the front of the head as tightly as the back, a thin slit of transparent perspex traversing the mask from side to side like a grin in the wrong place and revealing the burning eyes of whatever it was that lay within.

After that initial second of terror, Emma realised that it was only somebody wearing one of the gimmick mackintoshes from Paris which had high collars buttoning right across the face into the hood, with one transparent strip let in to allow the wearer to see where she was going.

But that second was enough. The faceless creature lunged forward. Plastic arms rose. Vulcanised gloves clawed—and before Emma had become fully aware of what was happening, her neck had been seized in a vice-like grip and her head forced downwards and under the water in the basin. The first indrawn breath of astonishment half filled her lungs with soapy water. She choked. She struggled and threshed. And desperately she tried to hold her breath . . .

But the grip was remorseless, the arms like steel bars. Despite her conscious attempt to prevent it, her diaphragm heaved in spasmodic contraction, her irritated lungs expanded, the muscles of her throat worked . . . and she swallowed another mouthful of soapy water, choking once more.

The total surprise of the attack was almost completely successful. Emma had been unprepared; whoever the assailant was, he or she was tremendously strong. There was a roaring in Emma's ears, a bursting and a pounding behind the eyes—and it doesn't take very long to drown a person taken by surprise and unsuspecting.

Emma had one card, though. And through the blackness

which threatened to engulf her, a bright point of reason in a corner of her mind screamed at her to play it—quickly.

She had won a Black Belt for *karate* when she lived for a time in Japan with her father.

The 3000-year-old self-defence system recognises 37 target areas on the body, in seven of which certain blows can be instantly fatal. Emma Peel, almost unconscious, bent forward with her head rammed into a basin by an opponent far bigger and stronger than she was, could be sure of reaching only two of these areas from her present cramped position. And even then it was dubious if she could land correctly, since she could not see and must guess what parts of her assailant were where. But it was the only chance she had . . .

Despairingly, she summoned her fast failing strength for a final effort. She made a strange twisting, flicking movement backwards with her left elbow. It landed on something soft behind the plastic. There was an astonished gasp.

The grip on Emma's neck slackened.

Instantly, rolling forward, as it were, further into the basin, Emma executed a kind of half-somersault, gripping the sides of the porcelain sink with both hands and straightening her right leg backwards and upwards with jarring force.

The sole of her foot connected—hard. There was rather a dreadful grunt — an exclamation of extreme pain on the indrawn breath—a frozen moment of suspense . . . and then the world-filling clatter of a heavy body collapsing as dead weight to the ground.

Emma fell off the basin on to the floor sobbing for breath. She retched and choked, sitting on the cool tiles and leaning her head against the wall as she painfully dragged air back into her tortured lungs. Tears of pain and vexation and reaction streamed down her face.

Eventually, she opened her eyes, suddenly fearful that she might be attacked again—to see the yellow raincoat painfully dragging itself up the wall and through the small window admitting light to a toilet whose door stood open. The attacker had had enough.

So had Emma. She hadn't the strength to pursue.

Wearily, she dragged herself to her feet and began the task of trying to repair the damage to her face and hair. In the end, she nearly missed her plane. They had called the flight three times before she emerged—wondering still why nobody had entered the cloakroom all this time.

The reason was simple. An *Out of Order* notice had been hung on the door since she entered . . .

In the interim, however, the papers had obviously been distributed. When the big, close-cropped man at the high desk gave her back her passport, he slammed it down on the wood before her. "I hope you travel by BEA, madam," he grated. "They tell me the washroom accommodation is superb . . ."

9

THE STORIES THAT NEVER WERE

STEED was waiting for Emma when she emerged from the customs hall at London Airport. Still shaken from her experience, she looked weak and tired, the pallor of her flawless features contrasting with the brown suit and the dark mane of auburn hair.

"My dear Mrs Peel," Steed exclaimed, solicitously taking her by the elbow and piloting her through the crowd around the arrival boards, "what *has* happened? You look as though you had seen a ghost."

"I almost did," Emma said grimly. "My own."

She reached into her bag and handed him the copies of the *Courier* which she had acquired at Schipol. "I did know," he said after a quick glance at the headlines. "Thus the question about the ghost—I was speaking journalistically. As you can imagine, the bells have been ringing and the wires humming again . . but you look full of news. Tell me."

Briefly, Emma recounted what had happened to her at the airport.

"Yes, I see," Steed mused when she had finished. "Somebody must have noticed you ferreting about in the freight shed, I suppose, and then decided that, since you had taken copies of the paper, you must be in one way or another on their track . . . Nuisance. What with this and the phone call Lindale made to me, it looks as though both our covers are likely to be blown. Still—we'd better go through with it, just in case."

"Here's another just-in-case," Emma said frostily.

"I beg your pardon?"

"Just in case it should happen to occur to you to ask whether there's any permanent damage, or if I feel any better, and I don't happen to be around at the time—you might care to file the fact in the computer you use for a brain that there wasn't and I do. A little."

"But of *course*! How remiss of me!" Steed was overflowing with false contrition. "You shouldn't attempt the heavy sarcasm for at least another ten years yet, though. It doesn't come off and it sounds pompous."

Emma maintained a cold silence across the rest of the busy hall, down the escalator and out into the open air. It was still hot, close and damp, but the sun had disappeared: everything had blurred into a muddy haze. There had been thunderstorms and gales on the coast—Emma had had quite a bumpy trip across the sea, in fact—but the weather had yet to break in London.

They crossed the approach road where the buses to the air-port terminal pulled in and walked under the long shelter pro-tecting those waiting for cars or taxis. Emma's ill humour disappeared as soon as she saw what lay beyond. Towering over them like a grasshopper among black beetles, Steed's Bentley glittered resplendently at the head of the queue of cabs —parked neatly and precisely beneath the notice warning *Reserved for taxis—No Parking*.

She laughed aloud. "Only you would dream of flouting the parking regulations of Europe's largest airport," she protested, "and, what's more, getting away with it!"

"Nonsense, my dear," Steed said. "All the spaces in the regular parking areas were taken—and one really cannot be expected to tool off to those *murderously* expensive Ministry of Works places about three counties away."

He shifted his grasp on the umbrella so that his hand was closed around the shaft near the ferrule, and hooked its handle in a special way around the handle of the Bentley's passenger door. A moment later, the shallow door was open and he was handing Emma in to the front seat.

"You must have very strong wrists, Steed," Emma said.

"Oh, I don't know," the undercover man replied modestly. "One used to manage a tolerable drive off the back foot, one supposes."

On the way back to town in the Bentley, Steed ran over the latest developments. "I had chaps staked out at every con-ceivable vantage point—and some inconceivable ones, if only you knew," he said. "And not one of them reported a thing. The editions of all three papers we were watching ran through as planned. My chaps scrutinised them at all stages. When they left the loading bays, they were precisely as designed and written.

I think, therefore, we have to admit as a fact that our previous theories were wrong.

"Despite the fact that none of the watchers noticed anything, the papers—or at least one of them—*were* tampered with again.

"And that proves to my satisfaction that the faking must be done *after* the completed editions leave Fleet Street, and not in the newspaper buildings themselves after all."

"Do we have to start looking for the fakers on the Continent again after all? Could Carew be right?" Emma asked.

"I don't think so. The impossibilities of this—and they were im*poss*ibilities and not im*prob*abilities—have been too clearly stated to need repeating: Creighton, Borridale himself and Lindale were all unshakeable on the point. I've been investigating times and opportunities and I think they were right."

"I suppose we'd better start charting their progress from the time they leave the offices to the time they're put on sale on continental streets, then," Emma said. "And then perhaps we can find the most likely point at which they could be, as they say, interfered with."

Steed nodded. "And I'd like to know, just as a matter of interest," he said, "exactly why three papers were involved before, but only the *Courier* this time. There must be some common denominator, some relevant factor which was missing in their cases this time but present before. And for that matter, why only these three papers at any time? Why none of the others, ever? I wish we had a computer available—I'd love to feed in all, *all* the information we could possibly dig up, and then ask it what *were* the common factors in such a context . . ."

"You're welcome to spend the night in my wardrobe, if you wish," Emma said.

"An entrancing thought, Mrs Peel. But your wardrobe computer would probably tell me that it was because the editor of the *Gazette* had never worn a leather tie or something."

"There's no need to be rude, Steed—Oh! *Look out!*"

"A bagatelle," Steed murmured, swerving the Bentley expertly round a car negotiating a roundabout in the wrong direction with a flick of his gloved wrists. "Belgian, you see. The worst drivers in Europe . . ."

He was worrying, nevertheless, more than he cared to say about the sheer *mechanics* of the newspaper faking. Whoever was doing it was getting bolder. To have switched a fake story into the *first* editions that Emma had seen in Amsterdam meant this time that the tampering must have been done *before* the event which had been misreported had actually occurred. For the editions had been printed and had left the *Courier* building before the Foreign Secretary had even begun to speak. This was a new departure—and a dangerous precedent.

Perhaps, though, it contained a clue inasmuch as there might be some special reason why this could be done at the *Courier* and not at either of the other two papers usually affected.

Steed decided that he must return to his flat to work it out. After dropping Emma in Fleet Street to make her report on the cosmetics reception, therefore, he drove back to Westminster Mews and began puzzling afresh over the page torn from *Hemming's* that he had discovered in Lindale's hand. Was it connected with the evidence the sub had wanted to show him or not? Was it a piece of the jigsaw that he couldn't see how to fit in—or was it an irrelevancy?

Indirectly, it was Emma who solved that particular problem in the end.

Marjorie Halloran was indulging in her usual fulmination against the fashion editor when she reached the office. "I mean, honestly," she said, waving a nicotine-stained hand at Emma, "when you've been working on something for nearly two weeks and got a complete exclusive into the bargain—*with* pictures, mind you—it's a bit too ruddy much when the whole wretched thing has to be slashed to a couple of hundred words at the foot of the page, minus illustrations, just because some beastly queer who takes you-know-who out to lunch launches a new tennis dress . . ."

"What's the matter," Emma asked with an amused smile. "Lost the page top *again*?"

"Lost the whole beastly page, ducky. Again. And we had a half page picture of some starving ghoul in a bikini only *yesterday*. Why we have to give space to these brainless chicks when what the readers want is advice on how to make *themselves* presentable, I do not know . . ."

Emma sat down at her table, exchanged a conspiratorial smile with Samantha, and took her notes out of her bag.

"Oh, my God, yes!" the beauty editor exclaimed. "You've just got back from Holland, haven't you? How was it?"

"It was fine."

"Can you make anything of it, d'you think, ducky? I'd like to run a piece tomorrow if you could. They're awfully nice people and they do advertise a lot, you know."

"Yes, I think so. There was some very interesting stuff there—one or two good ideas, too."

"Splendid! We want more beauty features in the paper, *I* think. If only the powers-that-be would realise this—and let us print pictures of *real* people looking lovely . . . like you, for example . . . Oh, well. You'd better do me your piece, Emma. About five hundred, I should think. Chatty. You know . . . And you'd better do your exes and get me to sign them right away, or the accounts bods'll never pay them before the end of the week."

"Right," Emma said. "There's just one thing. D'you think I could spend a half hour in the library looking at back numbers —just to get the house style, you know? Most of the work I've been doing has been for glossies and they're so breathlessly breathless that one has to think a bit before coming back to earth for a real newspaper—if you see what I mean."

"But of course, my pet," Marge Halloran said. "Do go along and browse. You'll soon pick up the peculiarly squalid kind of camp that passes for 'intimate' here. Don't forget those exes before four, though."

Emma sat for a while in the library—which shared with the endless rows of news files the greater part of the first floor—looking at back numbers of the *Courier*. Each day's issue, all five editions, was filled with those of the other six days of that week on a device rather like those used in the cafés of Vienna —a mixture of handle, rack and file that permitted the reader to lift up the week's editions in a single go and browse through each without disturbing the pages of the others.

Now that she had the opportunity, she turned up the issues for the three occasions on which perverted versions of the Foreign Secretary's speeches had been sold abroad. The copies of the paper on file, of course, were the genuine reports—not the forged ones sold on the Continent.

As she read the run-of-the-mill paragraphs, she began idly to wonder what had happened when the forgeries were inserted. If the forgers had "dispensed with" the main front-page story in each case and substituted a blown up version of Carew's speech—what had happened to the space where the speech was reported in the genuine editions? Presumably even a forged edition would hardly carry the same story twice—once unimportant on the back page; once importantly on the front! Therefore the holes from which these stories had been "lifted" must, in the forged editions, have been filled with something else . . .

The question was—what else? Had anyone thought of looking?

She rang Steed, but there was no reply from his flat. All right, she thought; she would act on her own initiative. No doubt her immediate colleagues on the beauty desk were totally unaware of the real reason for her presence on the *Courier*'s staff—but surely the managing editor must know she was working with Steed? How else would she have been able to get the "job" so quickly? Very well, then—she would act accordingly.

Emma was a woman almost spectacularly without guile. If there was a direct way of doing a thing, she would do it that way. If it were possible to ask a question without concealing any of the truth, that's the way she would ask it. The half-truths, equivocations and elisions that were Steed's stock-in-trade were totally foreign to her.

She took the lift, therefore, to Creighton's office and knocked on the outer door.

Sandra Gillan opened the door. She was wearing a suit of dove grey suede with a high neck and braid frogging in the style of an eighteenth century military uniform.

"Yes?" she said insolently, raising her blonde brows.

"I'd like to see Mr Creighton, please," Emma said firmly.

"Well I hardly think—Do we know you? I don't seem to have seen you before?"

"I've only been here two days. I'm working with John Steed on this business of the forged speech reports. Would you please tell Mr Creighton I'd like a word with him?"

Sandra Gillan was a very beautiful girl with a strong mind of her own, an arrogant manner and the certainty that her will would seldom be gainsaid. Emma Peel was a very beautiful woman with an equally strong mind of her own, a manner whose imperiousness was disguised by charm, and the quiet conviction lent by several centuries of ancestors bred to command. The battle was none the less real for being under the surface.

And, true to the form book, the thoroughbred was the victor.

Sandra Gillan dropped her eyes. "If you'll wait a moment," she said stiffly, "I'll go and see if he's in." She turned on her heel and disappeared into the inner office.

A few seconds later, she was back. "Will you please come this way?" she asked woodenly, preceding Emma in the direction of Creighton's inner sanctum. "Mrs Peel," she announced, throwing the door open perhaps a shade too vigorously.

"Thank you *so* much," Emma gushed as she swept past.

Creighton had his back to the door. He was studying one of the teleprinters ranged across the room under the windows. Eventually he swung round on his heel and looked at her speculatively.

"Mrs Peel?" he said on a rising inflection, his moist lips caressing the syllables. "My secretary tells me that you are working with Mr Steed."

"That's right, Mr Creighton. I've been, shall we say, seconded to the beauty desk while I'm here."

"Have you indeed? I know nothing of this arrangement—it must have been made directly by the proprietor. Not that I doubt your *bona fides* for a moment, Mrs Peel: you would be a very foolish girl to represent yourself as working for Mr Steed if that were not in fact the case . . . However, that is not the point at this minute, is it? What can I do for you, Mrs Peel?"

"I'm making various check comparisons—narrowing down the field, you know—and I'd very much like to have a look at the examples you have of the faked *Couriers* sold on the Continent on the three times prior to today."

"I see." The Managing Editor looked at her again in silence, his fleshy lower lip caught between the two large centre teeth prominent in his top jaw. Abruptly, he made up his mind. "Just wait a second, will you?" he asked. "I'll go and see if we can locate them for you."

Emma heard the sound of low voices in the outer office, and then he was back. "I'm frightfully sorry, Mrs Peel," he said regretfully. "All the copies of the bogus first editions we have over here are being photographed—for file purposes, you know, in case the originals should be mislaid or destroyed—and the reference library tell me the photographic department can't make them available before tomorrow morning."

"Oh, that's all right," Emma said at once. "I'm sorry to have bothered you. I'll drop by, if I may, and ask to see them tomorrow, then."

"I'm afraid you can't do that, Mrs Peel," the editor said softly.

"Oh. Why not?"

"Perhaps it has escaped your memory—you must be very busy—but today is Friday."

"It hadn't. But I still don't see—"

"If today is Friday, then tomorrow is Saturday. And since the *Courier* brings out no paper on Sunday, then nobody is required to work on Saturdays. Ergo, Mrs Peel, there will be nobody here tomorrow. The building will be closed. You will have to wait until Sunday or Monday to see your papers, I am afraid."

"Of course," Emma muttered, feeling like a schoolgirl caught cheating in an exam. "How stupid of me! I'll ask you for them again on Sunday, then."

"Just ring Miss Gillan when you come in," Creighton said, turning back to his teleprinter, "and she'll have them sent down to you . . ."

Sandra Gillan was examining her perfectly polished oval nails as Emma passed through her office on the way out. She didn't look up but there was a faint smile curling the corners of her full lips.

Emma shrugged and headed for the lifts.

Steed was less phlegmatic when she recounted the incident to him over dinner later that evening. "But that's utterly ridiculous," he cried, setting down his glass of Chambolle Musigny with care.

"It's certainly a little vexing, as we wanted to see the things," Emma said, looking at him curiously. "But I don't see why you—"

"No, no. You don't understand, my dear," Steed said. "The point is, I know the papers have *already* been photographed for file purposes. I've actually seen one of the photostats. Are you doing anything tomorrow evening?"

"Nothing that can't be postponed. Why?"

"I'd like your help in a little expedition," Steed said, picking up his glass again and sniffing appreciatively. "It seems to me there may be something about those originals that we aren't supposed to see. Therefore I feel it would be folly to wait until

Sunday. Something might—er—happen to them, don't you think? No—we'll anticipate events a bit and look at them to-morrow after all."

"But I've just told you, Steed—"

"Patience, my dear. Patience . . . By Jove, Gregory was right! This forty-eight *is* rather splendid! . . . Tomorrow night we are going to burgle the offices of our employer . . ."

10

A KILLER IN THE LIFT

GETTING into the building itself did not present much of a problem. Steed and Emma left the Bentley in a cul-de-sac off Fetter Lane and walked through the deserted side streets to the back entrance of the *Courier* building. The whole area, normally busier at night than during the day, with every opening liable to echo to the pounding and clatter of printing machinery, was shuttered and quiet. Darkness had just fallen and the few lights that showed high up on the cliff-like faces of the buildings served only to underline the emptiness of the streets below. It was still very close, the atmosphere sulphurous and heavy.

Steed had decided that their best plan was to avoid Borridale Court altogether and get in somewhere near the loading bay, where they would be under cover and thus that much safer from detection.

It turned out to be a wise move. There was a small pass door let into one of the huge iron gates blocking off the bay when the building was closed, and this, Steed thought, would present little difficulty if he could manage five or six minutes alone with the lock.

"First of all, though," he said, "there are one or two little things like burglar alarms to disconnect. If you could possibly go to the corner there and keep watch on the street, I'd feel a little more certain of being able to work uninterrupted . . ."

The covered way leading to the bay pierced the building from back to front. Emma went to the front exit first and glanced out into Borridale Court. She was all in black: glove-soft leather boots, and a skin-tight jersey cat-suit with a V-shaped front in ciré which rippled with highlights as she moved. Steed flicked a speck of dust from the lapel of his navy pin-stripe suit as he watched her lope back.

"I'd love to have seen the setting you fed your computer control to produce that ensemble," he said with a smile. "What

96

kind of occasion do you call *this*, for example?"

"I just breathe the word 'Steed' into a special speaking tube," Emma said, "and the computer gives up. All the doors open at once, and I'm given a free hand to choose what I want! . . . The courtyard in the front's completely clear. Even the lord's Rolls is away."

"Yes, he's gone for the weekend," Steed said. "Splendid. Keep watch on the back now, and I'll get started."

Emma went to the back entrance of the covered way, looked out into the lane beyond, and turned round to give Steed the thumbs-up sign. He nodded, hooked his umbrella over one arm, and produced what looked like a flat, silver cigarette case from an inside pocket. Once opened, however, the case presented a surprising interior: ranged neatly along each side a dozen or more high-precision instruments in miniature gleamed dully in the reflected light from the street lamps outside. Steed pulled two away from their clips and began to trace the course of an insulated wire leading from the bell of a burglar alarm.

Two minutes later there was a sharp click. One of the wires was severed and the other appeared to be earthed in some way through the use of a shunt fashioned from one of Steed's instruments.

He moved swiftly to the door then. Dropping to a crouching position he examined the two locks and their keyholes.

Once more the flat metal case was produced. He considered its contents in silence for a moment, then selected a bright tool, which he tried in the top lock. Shaking his head, he withdrew it, replaced it in the case and tried with another. This, too, was evidently unsuitable. So was the third. But after a little manipulation, the fourth turned stiffly and a tumbler snicked home. The lower lock was no trouble: it succumbed at the first try. Slowly, he swung the pass door open and stepped through into the loading bay.

Everything was dark inside. A few sheeted shapes loomed up in the faint illumination filtering through from the covered way, but beyond Steed could see nothing. Returning to the door, he beckoned Emma, retrieved his tools and re-connected the burglar alarm. Once she was in, he shut the door and felt in his inside pocket again. A moment later the beam of a small flash-light lanced the gloom; it had hardly any spread but a great deal of penetration.

With its help, they negotiated the islands of machinery bulked formidably against the blackness, stepped over obstructions in the floor and skirted the great presses themselves. After the distant noises of the city which had been ever-present outside, the utter silence of the deserted machine room was oppressive. The air seemed dank and chill, the sour, flat smell of greased metal stronger than ever. Oil-smooth highlights slid over the contours of machines as they moved the torch, winking coldly and brightly back from casings and plates and steely shafts. Eventually, Steed located a darker patch amongst the blackness.

"That's the opening to the staircase," he said. "We'll go carefully up to the foyer and reconnoitre."

Light streamed through the glass doors of the entrance hall from the lamps in Borridale Court, etching the shapes of desk, lecterns, clock and lifts against the neutral tone of the walls. The uprights between the large panes of glass cast iron-sharp shadows across the floor. The court itself was still untenanted, and beyond it the boundary of Greening's Row was marked by a windowless wall.

"And it's just as well," Steed said soberly. "At night, anyone in here must be like a goldfish in a bowl to a watcher outside! Do you think the *Courier* switches off all its electricity at the mains on Saturdays?"

"I really couldn't say. Why do you ask?"

"Because, my dear, if they do not, then we shall be able to use a lift; but if they do, then we won't."

"Oh."

"In either case, we'd better get out of this glass cage as soon as possible."

Steed walked carefully and quickly along a bar of shadow thrown by the upright between two doors. At the lift block, he turned back to Emma. "I'll try the left-hand one," he said, "because—"

"—because the centre one goes so much more slowly!" Emma finished in chorus with him. Her black-clad figure moved up to him along the same pathway of shadow. He pushed the button.

The gates of the left-hand lift rumbled smoothly back; the indicator light came on; Steed and Emma stepped inside; the gates closed again—and the light on the indicator column above the doors went out, came on again a floor higher up, went out, re-lit two floors higher . . . three floors . . . four floors higher. And stopped at the fifth.

Tiger-striped with bars of light falling through frosted glass partitions from the street lamps outside, the fifth floor corridor led to the Process Department. "They make the blocks for the paper here," Steed said, pausing outside the locked door. There was a loud click. "Ah! — Now where might they keep copies of the paper that were being duplicated for library purposes," he mused aloud, threading his way between shallow sinks and baths of acid and electric furnaces decorated with dials and piping.

Wherever it was, they couldn't locate it—nor did they see any sign, physically or as a ledger entry, that the copies they sought had been there. "That merely means that no blocks or automatic means of reproducing the fake copies have been used," Steed said. "Let's try the photo library anyway—to see if the blasted papers have been copied at all!"

"We'll have to go down to the first again, then," Emma said.

"No, love. Up one to the sixth. The first floor is *the* library —where the editorial boys look up the news files and the cuttings to get all the background they can on a man or a story. And where they see what's *available* in the way of photographs. But the photo library proper is different—or at least it is here. It's where they keep all the originals, the negatives, the picture features for syndication and so on. They have adopted the Wastermund system for organising—"

"I know. I've read page five hundred and three of Kennedy Smiley, too," Emma interrupted. "'As with catalogues for university libraries, different kinds of newspapers may adopt different lay-outs for their various departments. Photographic above Process above Printing above Editorial is a common floor arrangement, but those with the "open" newsroom rather than a series of compartments may prefer their library organisation . .' and so on, and so on."

"If you have such a good photographic memory, you might as well stay here. You should do well," Steed said. "As for me, I'm going to nip up the stairs to the floor above to see how well Wastermund has been—er—interpreted."

But the photo library proved as unhelpful as the Process. After a half hour scrutinising catalogues, lists, classifications and innumerable folders in the steel drawers of filing cabinets, all in the limited beam of Steed's torch, they had found nothing.

They climbed two more flights of stairs to the eighth floor. Another door was expertly burgled, and they were in Sandra Gillan's office. There was nothing there either, nor was there anything in Creighton's room beyond. "As I suspected," Steed said—and it was hard to tell if he was pleased or disappointed— "But we had to make sure that they were telling the truth and the papers weren't in either of these offices."

"Why don't we actually look *in* the photographic department?" Emma asked at last. "Although *we* know the photography took place some time ago because you've seen the result of it, someone might have told the Managing Editor the job wasn't completed yet, for some reason. I mean, he probably *had* been told that they wouldn't be ready until Sunday. The thing is—who'd been telling him? And in any case, I think it's worth taking a look just in case, don't you?"

Steed took her by the arm. "For a rugger player," he said, "you sometimes display an unexpectedly feminine approach. A mere man would never dream of looking in the place he was *told* they'd be . . ."

With the dying beam of the flashlight, they probed their way down the dark stairs to the seventh floor again. Inside the photographic department, its enfeebled rays picked out developing tanks, more sinks, an enlarger resembling an atom-splitting machine, straw-covered carboys of acid, rolls of developed film pegged out on a line to dry—and a guillotine surrounded by piles of photographic papers. The acrid smells of the darkroom mingled with the thin stink of chemicals to weigh down the oppressive atmosphere even more. There was another odour, too—familiar but out of context, surely? A kind of . . . More like a sort of . . .

"There's something been burning!" Emma cried aloud, and she spun round and dashed to a steel waste bin under a work bench at the far side of the big room. Steed hurried across, shielding the wan light of the torch from the windows with one hand.

The bin held a quantity of ashes. The remnants, it seemed, of several whole newspapers which had been burned in it. The grey paint had blistered at the bottom and there were soot marks up one side. Steed picked out a fragment of paper that had not been entirely consumed. "Yes," he said, "as I feared: that's it! These are the copies—these *were* the copies, I should say!—of the fake continental editions we are looking for. And what's more—Good Lord!"

"What is it, Steed?" Emma asked. "What's the matter?"

"These ashes are still warm," Steed said slowly. "Look—one of the pieces is still smouldering and giving off smoke . . ."

"You mean . . . ?"

"I mean they must have been burned only a matter of minutes ago—certainly long after we had entered the building."

"And that means?"

"There are other people here besides us. And they must know we are here. If the papers have only just been burned, it can only be because otherwise we would have found them—and also it must mean that, had we *not* been about to find them, they might have been left. Otherwise why not destroy them days ago?"

"But why destroy them at all?" Emma objected. "It's not as if they were the only examples, after all. There must be hundreds still in existence on the Continent, and probably several other copies of each over here—if one knew where to look for them!"

"Exactly. Therefore the reason must be time. To stop us getting hold of them *for the time being*. To delay us finding out whatever they have to show us until after the weekend, I suppose."

"Something must be about to break, then."

"Yes. What worries me more, frankly, is the timing of this little incineration. The fact that the papers have only just been burned suggests that someone knew we were about to discover them, as I said. But that, in its turn, has to mean that we have been watched—and that the decision to destroy the copies was only taken after it had become clear where we were heading."

"D'you think your flat has been watched, then?"

"I think it must have been. And I'm kicking myself for not spotting it. It's just that I hadn't realised there was that sort of urgency about the job at all."

"Presumably someone must have overtaken us on the way here from Westminster Mews, then, and slipped into the building ahead of us?"

"Or telephoned ahead to tip confederates off. I prefer to think it was that—we rarely get *overtaken* in the Bentley."

"But if a watcher merely saw us leave the mews, he wouldn't *know* we were coming hère. Unless your *coq au vin* was bugged of course."

A shadow clouded Steed's brow. "You can take it from me, our little dinner was mike-free," he said. "One does have a routine about checking for such things."

"Then how would they know?"

"Perhaps they telephoned just in case—and then *followed* us to make sure."

"Really, Steed," Emma said, "sometimes you're just like a little boy!"

"Unlike a little boy, I know when it's braver to run away than stay and face the music. An empty newspaper building on a Saturday night could house an army of assassins. Let's go!"

They hurried out of the photographic department and along the corridor to the lifts. Steed jabbed the button of the left-hand one with the ferrule of his umbrella.

Nothing happened.

He pressed again. In the silence which rang throughout the great building, the complementary buzz that sounded on the control panel of the lift car floated clearly up the shaft. But the lift didn't move.

"Somebody's opened the outer gates to immobilise it," Steed said. "They can't have cut the current: it wouldn't buzz in the first place, and secondly the indicator light would have gone off. Look—there it is still at five . . ." As he spoke, there was a muffled rolling noise followed by a thump. Then, ominous and unmistakable, a deep, ascending whine.

Somebody was coming up in the other lift . . .

The bulbs on the central indicator column flashed and changed—from G to 1, from 1 to 2 . . . And suddenly their eyes were dazzling in a blaze of light. The landing lamps from top to bottom of the huge building had been switched on.

Grabbing Emma by the hand, Steed was already running. "Come on," he panted, "we've got to move . . . this means there's at least two of them . . . one in the lift and one for the lights . . . and presumably they have a right to be here, or they wouldn't dare have the lights on at all . . ."

They clattered down the first flight of stairs which wound around the lift shaft all the way down to the foyer.

"Our lift's at the fifth," Steed gasped. "That's two floors down

—and we must reach it, if we can, before the one coming up does." They turned the corner and pounded down the second flight to gain the sixth floor. The light on the lift indicator column was just changing from 3 to 4.

"They go on with a main switch, but you can switch them *off* on individual floors," Steed said, lunging Hamlet-wise with his umbrella at a button light-switch. "Have at *thee*!" The lights on that landing went out.

They hurled themselves at the first of the two flights joining the sixth and fifth floors. The whine of the lift was very loud now. As they ran down, the great black counterweight overtook them and sank soundlessly past into the depths. Rounding the half-landing at the back of the shaft for the final flight, Steed abruptly stopped in full flight, grabbing Emma just in time to stop her sailing past and down to the fifth floor.

The three shafts were to their right. In the farthest, the immobilised car stood, both inner and outer gates wedged open with a metal waste bin. The nearest was empty, presumably with the out-of-order lift in it at ground floor level. And up the centre shaft, the roof of the darkened car was just rising slowly into view.

"Too late, blast it!" Steed hissed. "Back here! Quickly!" He dragged her round the corner on to the half-landing behind the shafts, where they were screened by the shaft wall and by the back of the lift car itself, which was not caged like the gate and sides, but of solid metal sheeting. As they dodged back, there was a bright flash from the rising lift. A sharp, flat detonation thundered in the stairwell with appalling force.

"Shooting, eh!" Steed muttered grimly. "I was afraid of that. They're firing something in a heavy calibre, too. That sounded like a Luger."

Tensed together at the corner, they listened to the continuing whine of the lift beyond the solid wall backing the shaft.

"Shall we make a run for it?" Emma asked. "Maybe we could make the left-hand car and free the doors before he can bring his lift down again . . ."

"No. Wait," Steed whispered. "The cars have solid backs and the well itself has this wall. So long as he's in a lift and we're on a half-landing behind the shaft, we're out of sight and out of range. But the moment we're on the actual stairs or a main landing, he can fire through the bars of the cages and we're sitting ducks. Or even dead ducks . . ."

"But the farther up or down he is, the more acute the angle of fire—and the more bars of the cage the bullet has to miss."

"Quite. So we keep as many as possible between us. We'll stay here until we see the way his mind works—then we act accordingly."

Somewhere above them, the lift stopped. They heard the automatic gates roll back, pause, and close again.

Silence.

After a moment, Steed leaned across and spoke quietly into Emma's ear. "Seventh floor, I think," he said. "He must have pressed the button for the one we were on. To reactivate the lift now, he'll either have to get out of the car and back in again—or jump up in the air."

"Jump up in the *air*?" Emma's whisper was incredulous.

"Yes. Haven't you noticed? When the last person leaves an automatic lift, as soon as their weight's taken off it, the floor rises against the spring-loading and breaks a contact. Then the weight of the next person getting in presses it down again and re-establishes the connection—when you can press a button and the lift'll work again. It won't do that unless the floor has risen and broken that contact."

"So if you take the lift to a floor but change your mind and don't get out . . .?"

"Exactly—you have to jump off the floor of the car to break that connection. Or else it won't answer to the button; the doors merely keep opening and closing at the same floor."

As though in illustration of his words, a scrambling thump echoed down from the shaft from above. They could hear the car shaking against its steel runners. Then, almost immediately afterwards, the whine of the lift descending again . . .

"Now?" Emma asked softly.

"Yes," Steed replied. "But *up*wards."

"Upwards?"

"Yes. He's not going to take his lift *below* the floor ours is jammed on. We'd just run down and get in. So he must be going *to* our floor. We've got to give him a reason to leave it. Come on!"

They pounded up the stairs to the sixth floor landing, hared past the lift gates, and made for the flight leading to the next half-landing. The bottom of the descending lift car loomed menacingly nearer as they ran. Just before they reached safety three more shots crashed out. One of the bullets spanged against the shaft cageing and ricocheted away down the corridor with a whine descanting over the noise of the lift.

"He was firing downwards," Steed said from the safety of the half landing. "Let's see how good his reactions are upwards." He hung his bowler on the crook of his umbrella and pushed it cautiously round the corner.

The report was almost instantaneous.

Steed hauled in the decoy and examined it. A small trapdoor had been opened in the crown. "That's a nuisance," he said. He pulled a small diary from his pocket and made an entry.

"What on earth are you doing?" Emma asked.

"Reminder. I'll have to fit in a trip to St James's first thing Monday morning to replace the hat." He scrutinised the punctured bowler again. "Pretty good shot," he murmured. "Upwards and to the left from a descending platform . . . Still—we must move again. He'll be back up. But he doesn't know we're not armed—and he'll be expecting us to wait here. Quietly, *please* . . ."

As they tiptoed down the stairs again and along the sixth floor corridor, they heard the lift shake to a halt, the doors open and close, and the jump of the occupant before he pressed the button again. Then once more the whine as it rose.

Since Steed's foray with his umbrella, the landing lights on the sixth floor had remained out. Reflected illumination from the floors above and below streamed from the shaft nevertheless and penetrated some distance down the shadowy corridor. In the dim light, they watched from the corner of the short passage leading to the photo library as the lift bounced to a halt at their floor. The gates opened and closed. But nothing else happened.

Inside the car, squat and amorphous as a spider, they could dimly make out a figure. The diffused light glinted from the barrel of an automatic, questing this way and that as the occupant of the lift turned from side to side.

"Is it anyone we know?" Emma whispered.

"Can't see," Steed replied, raking the landing and the lift with his keen eyes. "Whoever it is, is wearing a rough and ready disguise, as far as I can make out—a fireman's oilskin and a peaked cap by the look of it. The kind of thing even George Carew would be anonymous in."

"Leave this to me. I'll draw him," Emma said. She produced from the hip pocket of her suit the thin, flat compact she had been given in Holland. "I couldn't resist a couple of modifications," she added quietly. "The spring was so strong . . ." Holding the compact on end with the opening away from her, she sighted carefully along the corridor—then deliberately pressed the retractable catch on the back with her other hand.

Propelled by Emma's "rearrangement" of the powerful spring, the circular mirror shot out of the oyster-like mouth of the compact with the force of a projectile. It skimmed just below the corridor ceiling, above the eye-line of the watcher in the lift, and sliced into the glass panel topping the door at the far end of the corridor beyond the landing.

The panel shattered instantly, great shards of glass jangling to the floor—and the little mirror carried on into the room beyond it, either hitting a typewriter or knocking the receiver off a telephone, for a small bell shrilled distinctly.

The effect was remarkable—both so far as sheer noise in the silent building was concerned, and also in its direct result.

The lift doors rolled back and, like a spider summoned to the far end of its web by the vibrations of a trapped insect, the gunman shuffled hastily out, waddling off to the far end of the passage in his bizarre disguise.

Steed and Emma acted in perfect concert. Together, they flitted behind him from their hiding place to the landing. Emma, at a nod from the undercover man, ran lightly down the stairs to free the doors of the immobilised lift, while Steed himself stepped one foot inside the still-open doors of the gunman's car, pressed down with it to lower the floor, and then drew back as the doors slid shut.

He watched the oilskinned back warily. The man would have expected the doors to close after a pause. What he had to do next depended on the fellow not turning round. At the moment, he was flattened against the wall, peering round the corner by the door with the shattered glass, his gun at the ready.

With infinite care, Steed raised his umbrella. The lift was, as it were, primed now; it would obey a press on any button or a summons from any floor. Meticulously, he poked the umbrella through the bars until the ferrule rested against the button marked 16. Firmly and steadily, he pressed.

The lift jerked abruptly into motion. Its initial acceleration was greater than he had bargained for, and he was unable to withdraw the umbrella in time. As the trellis of the inner gates shot upwards past the stationary bars of the outer, the handle was wrenched from his grasp and the shaft whisked up and snapped like a carrot. In half a second the umbrella was reduced to a mangled bundle of splintered wood and metal festooned with silk rags. One or two pieces fluttered casually down the shaft.

At the same time, Steed flung himself back to the stairwell and down the flight towards the fifth floor, the gunman whirled towards the lifts, the big automatic in his hand spitting flame, and Emma called *"Right"* from the landing below.

As the empty car whined its fruitless way up to the 16th floor, feet pounded heavily along the corridor. Somewhere, far above, somebody else was running too. A female voice cried something hoarse and unintelligible down the lift shaft.

Steed had turned the corner at the foot of the first flight of stairs and gained the shelter of the half-landing before the gunman reached the shaft to find the lift gone and the birds flown. He was visible through four sets of bars as he ran down the last flight, however, and the man tried three more snapshots as he went. The undercover man could hear them thungging off the metal bars of the cage.

Before crossing the fifth floor landing to reach the doors that Emma was holding open for him, Steed pressed the switch to extinguish the landing lights. There was no point in taking chances!

From the floor above, a distinctive snick told him that the man with the gun had pushed a fresh clip into his automatic. The fusillade of shots which crashed out as he leaped for the lift did not surprise him, therefore. What he hadn't expected was the series of heavier, deeper explosions from farther up: the gunman's accomplice on a higher floor was emptying a revolver down the lift shaft.

"My goodness me," Steed panted as he catapulted into the car and leaned against the back wall gasping for breath, "I haven't experienced anything like this since my cousin Edgar got into the doubles finals of a college of theology tennis tournament."

Emma pressed the button for the basement. "I can't say I see the connection," she said politely as the doors closed and the lift sank towards the ground.

"Canons to the right of him, Canons to the left of him, volleyed and thundered," Steed explained apologetically.

"I'm glad that this car has a metal roof," Emma said after a decent interval. "But in a way one's glad of the shots from above, too. It means that the second person—the one who must have put on the lights when our friend with the gun came up in the lift—is above us and not below us."

"True," Steed said. "Unless there's a third—and a fourth!"

"Surely, if there were any more, they'd have shown themselves by now?"

"Probably. But we'll have to take care getting out."

The lift dropped past the fourth, third and second floors. Each stretched deserted and empty in the bright glare of the landing lights. The shooting, which had continued for several more seconds after the car started to move, had stopped. The would-be murderers above had given it up. Steed took out his notebook again and started to write.

"What is it this time?" Emma asked in amused exasperation.

"I lost my umbrella," Steed said mildly. "At least, it's not so much the loss of the brolly I mind, as of the sword that was inside it." He finished writing and put the book away. "Watch out now," he said. "The outer doors in the machine room, like those on the ground floor, are solid—so we shan't be able to see what's in store for us until they open. If you have any more toys like that rocket-firing flapjack, prepare to use them now!"

"Only a lipstick atomiser filled with ammonia," Emma said.

But the lift doors in the basement slid back on a blackness as profound as that through which they had entered. No livid flame spat at them from behind the presses; no coshes descended upon their apprehensive heads; no rush of feet ambushed them amongst the machinery. With the help of the feeble glimmer remaining in Steed's torch, they negotiated the machine room and gained the street via the pass door they'd broken in by.

"You know there must be some pretty definite clue in those papers," Steed said. "Or they'd never take so much trouble trying to stop us seeing them—which can only be a temporary setback, anyway, as far as we're concerned. They must know we shall be able to get others on Monday. Things are hotting up, and time must be of the utmost importance to them. I'm convinced something's due to happen *before* Monday—so I'm not going to wait until then and go through official channels. I know where copies of those papers are and I want to see them *tonight*. I take it you're prepared for a second little essay at the gentle art of burglary?"

He looked back and upwards as they walked through the silent streets towards Fetter Lane. The *Courier* building was in total darkness again. All the lights had been put out.

A sultry glare in the sky over the West End silhouetted the roofs of the warehouses on the far side of Greening's Row. The few lights showing earlier seemed to have been extinguished. Absentmindedly, Steed took the girl's hand as they crossed the road.

"LOOK OUT!" Emma screamed.

The black Mercedes had two wheels on the pavement. She tightened her grip on Steed's fingers as it hurtled down on them, bending from the hips and dipping one shoulder. The undercover man flew over her back and crashed into the wall as she threw herself frantically in the opposite direction.

Missing them by fractions of inches, the heavy saloon thundered past, lurching back into the roadway to avoid a lamp standard. It slewed sideways for a moment as it hit the corner into Fetter Lane, was expertly corrected, and hissed off in the direction of High Holborn with a discreet roar from its exhaust. The car showed no lights but Emma had the impression as it flashed past that there were at least five people in it.

Steed picked himself up and cautiously felt himself all over. "Are you all right, Mrs Peel?" he called formally. Emma nodded from the far side of the road, brushing the dust from her suit where she had fallen. "*I'm* all right, Steed," she said, "but you just hit a wall! Is there any damage?"

Steed affected to examine the brickwork. "I don't think so," he replied. "So far as I'm concerned, a few bruises only—and this . . ." He held up one arm. There was a long tear running the length of his sleeve. "Another case for the notebook, I fancy . . . And thanks. It's nice not to be an entry in somebody else's notebook—even if you did have to demonstrate the art of judo to prevent it!"

There was a vivid zig-zag of lightning somewhere beyond Blackfriars. Almost immediately, thunder crackled across the gloomy sky. Huge, random drops of rain began to spot the pavement. Emma looked up into the night.

"Oh, no!" She exclaimed. "Oh, *no*—the first time I've ever seen you minus an umbrella, and there's going to be a cloudburst!"

11

WHAT THE BUTLER SAID

THE weather had broken at last. The oppressive heat and the
damp, close atmosphere which had been building up over
the windless city for the past two days had come to a head in the
biggest thunderstorm of the summer. The rash of raindrops
spotting the road when Steed and Emma started running
towards the Bentley had coalesced into a continuously damp
surface before they were half way to the cul-de-sac where he
had left the car. By the time they reached it, the gutters had
begun to run with water, and the rain was lancing down with a
blinding, grey intensity, splashing six inches high off the pavements and streaming in great cascades from cornice and awning
and gutter.

Another multiple fork of lightning seared across the eastern
sky as Steed struggled to erect the Bentley's touring hood. This
time, the thunder was louder, the gap between the two was
smaller still.

By the time the hood irons were all in and the black mohair
covering had been stretched over them and buttoned down to
the sides of the body, the pelting of the rain was almost tropical.
Lightning flickered intermittently and the roaring of the thunder
was with them all the time.

The job could have been done far more quickly had Steed
not chivalrously insisted that Emma sit inside the car under
the hood as it was put up, and had he not put on a raincoat he
kept in the car and worked one-handed while he held a spare
umbrella over his head with the other.

"But it *saves* time in the end, you know," he said in answer
to Emma's remark pointing this out. "It may take a little longer
actually erecting the hood, but at the end of it I remain—as
you can see—at least relatively dry." He settled himself into the
driving seat and pressed the starter.

"I'm afraid I can't quite see where the saving comes in,"

Emma said as the great engine wheezed once, coughed into life and then rumbled fruitily beneath their feet.

"Well, it means that we don't have to call back at Westminster Mews on the way."

"Call at your flat?"

"Yes. You're reasonably dry, too, aren't you?"

"I got wet enough running up here—but it's all fairly superficial. I'm not what I call really drenched, if you know what I mean. I shan't squelch when I walk!"

"Exactly. I'm in about the same condition. Damp but undeterred. So we don't have to call either at my place or yours—though we should do, mind, if we really were wet."

"What on earth are you talking about?"

"Well, we couldn't very well burgle the Foreign Office and leave great pools and rivulets of water and damp footprints all over the place, could we? We'd have to change."

"The Foreign Office? Burgle the *Foreign Office*? Steed, I hope you're joking . . ."

"I was never more serious, my dear—at least, very seldom."

"But surely you *can't* . . . I mean, a newspaper building—"

"Yes, yes," Steed interrupted, slipping the Bentley into first and nosing out of the cul-de-sac into the streaming wastes of Fetter Lane, "all very unorthodox, I know. One simply *doesn't* . . . and all that. But the only copies of the bogus editions of those papers that I *know* for certain are in London are filed in a department of the F.O. in Carlton House Gardens. And I need to see them tonight."

"But there must be some way—I mean, isn't there someone you could phone? Someone who could get you permission? You must be *entitled* to see them, after all."

"Oh, I am. And there is. But you seem to have forgotten that you're living back in a bureaucracy again. You tell me one permanent civil servant who'd take the responsibility of opening up a government office out of regular hours . . . They'd all say, yes, of course, old boy, but we'd just better check with old so-and-so. And old so-and-so'd say it was okay by him—provided whatsisname agreed. And in the end, you'd be exactly where you'd have been if you hadn't bothered at all—waiting outside the door of the department when it opened at ten o'clock on Monday morning."

"Well, I suppose you know what you're doing."

"Oddly enough, I do," Steed said. "Those papers don't count as secrets and they're not classified, so the sentence should be light." He edged the Bentley into one of the knots of traffic swishing up High Holborn. At New Oxford Street, the continuous drumming of the rain on the soft roof changed in character: the car reverberated from stem to stern to the pounding of gigantic hailstones. The pellets danced in a haze above the surface of the road, rattled like distant musketry on the coachwork and poured from the sky in such profusion that it was almost impossible to see.

Most of the traffic pulled in to the side of the road and stopped until conditions improved. But Steed coaxed the Bentley steadily on, peering through the narrow windscreen and muttering to himself as he scrubbed at the fast-forming condensation with the back of his hand.

Down Shaftesbury Avenue, the lightning blazed brighter than the garish shop fronts and neon signs which trailed their wavering reflections in the dark, shining cascades of the sidewalk. Small groups of people huddled in every doorway, entry and arcade, peering uncertainly upward into the fury of the storm.

South of Piccadilly, the streets were emptier still. The hail had been replaced by a relentless downpour of rain, though the centre of the storm seemed to have passed over and the thunder and lightning now grumbled and shimmered in the distance.

The Bentley splashed down the Haymarket and turned into Pall Mall. Steed drove round the car park by the Duke of York's Steps and bowled along Carlton House Terrace. Towards the far end, he switched off the engine and coasted to a halt in another cul-de-sac. For a moment, they sat in silence.

Under the broad-leaved chestnut trees, the car was protected from the driving rain and only an occasional large drop plopped from the saturated foliage to its sodden roof. Beyond some iron railings, a gutter which had become choked with leaves and twigs in the summer months had overflowed and now directed a noisy waterfall down the stucco side of a house. From somewhere on the far side of the building the sound of boozy singing and breaking glass cut through the drumming of the rain.

"The Savage Club must be having a smoker," Steed observed as he swung himself out of the car. "I think it's passing over a bit. Let's go."

They walked together in the shelter of his spare umbrella to the corner of the short street. The great cream terraces with their pediments and porticos stretched silent and unlit in each direction. The rain had indeed almost stopped now, leaving a mournful dripping from the branches as a memento of its visit.

"It's the Gardens, actually, and not the Terrace," Steed said. "I think it'll be easier if we—er—go in by the back entrance in the Mall rather than make a formal entry from the front."

He led her through a short, paved walk bordered with railings to a flight of steps leading down to the sandy ride under the plane trees which stretch from the Admiralty Arch to Buckingham Palace. A short way along towards Marlborough House, he stopped outside the single-storey basement projection which carries the ground-floor terraces of the splendid houses above and behind the trees. He looked up and down the dark tunnel of The Mall. Between the Palace and the Arch, gleaming wetly in their floodlights, not a soul was to be seen except the caped and shining policeman on point duty at the corner of the road leading to St James's Palace.

Steed nodded in a satisfied way and moved briskly towards a door with peeling paint that was flanked by two iron-barred windows.

There didn't seem to be much trouble about breaking into this particular department of the Foreign Office, Emma thought as she meekly followed Steed down dusty passages, up wooden stairs, across deeply carpeted halls and then up again—via more graceful stairs curling around a white painted gallery this time—to a pleasantly furnished room with deep, shuttered windows on the first floor. None of the three doors that the undercover man had had to unlock appeared to give him much trouble.

Once in the room, he calmly switched on the central chandelier and walked over to a row of five green filing cabinets which stood in the space between the two french windows leading to the balcony.

Emma sat down at a polished table with a bowl of roses in the centre. She looked at the twelve by twelve deep-pile rug which covered most of the middle of the room. The pattern was the same as the one her father had had in the study at Monckton.

Steed was rummaging in one of the cabinets. "Sorry to keep

you," he called over his shoulder. "It's just a matter of whether the sub-classification is under B for bogus or F for fake. Or I suppose it *might* even be T for tampered-with or D for doctored . . ."

Emma was tired. She sighed. "Steed," she said, "are you *sure* it's all right . . . all this?"

He looked up, a cardboard folder in one hand. "All right? What?"

She made a vague gesture embracing the whole room. "All this. Breaking in, talking in a normal voice, putting the *lights* on, even . . ."

"Good Lord, yes! I've got a *right* to be here—inside. It's just the actual bit where one has to force an entry that's a bit dicey. Do you understand?"

"No."

"Well, it's just that one has the right to *be* here, but doesn't have the right to *get* here, if you see what I mean. So if one can't find the chap who can give the formal permission to cross the threshold, one tends to cut corners a little—*Ah*! Here we *are*!" He triumphantly pulled out a large green folder and carried it over to the table. In it were three copies of the *Courier*.

Steed moved the bowl of flowers and spread each one out on the polished wood.

"Now this whole operation—including our visit to the *Courier* —arises from a hunch of yours," he said. "It was you who wanted to check what was substituted for the genuine reports that were 'lifted' to the front page—and because no one would let you . . . that's why we're here. So you have a look now that we've tracked them down."

Emma leafed quickly through the three editions of the paper. "Well, here are the phoney stories," she said. "Five column banner at the top for the first one. Double column three-decker downpage for the next. And the big stuff page-top again this week. I have a note here where the original, genuine reports were in each edition." She produced a flat crocodile wallet and took out a folded piece of paper.

"Yes. Here we are. The first and the third were originally short pieces on the back page. The second was a filler on page two."

"Have you a note of exactly where they *were* on the page? I mean can you identify which of the short stories on the bogus back page is the substitute and which were there originally?"

"Oh, yes. I took fairly detailed notes when I was looking at the real stories in the *Courier* library—which column, how many inches down, how many lines long, and so on. That's when the idea came to me."

"Splendid," Steed said. "Let's have a look then."

They were able to identify the spaces easily from Emma's notes. As she had surmised, when the stories were "promoted" to the front page, the space left by their removal had in each case been filled by something quite different.

"As before, the first and third seem to be comparable, but the second seems to be somehow different," she said with a puzzled frown. "Look—the first hole has been filled by some story about a potholer in the West Country who had been presumed lost but had really been staying with his aunt in Devizes all the time. He just forgot to tell his wife."

She slid the third and most recent *Courier* across the table towards her, turned it over and pointed at the last column on the back page. "And this one, see, is the one about the man who divorced his wife to marry his secretary—and then advertised for a secretary, and the wife applied to the agency handling the ad and got the job. Remember, the *Mirror* ran a centre-page piece on it?"

Steed nodded. "One never seems to *meet* these people," he said.

"No, but these are typical of the sort of overmatter stories that would be stuffed into a middlebrow paper like the *Courier* to fill a hole," Emma said. "Not blown up as they would be in a tabloid, but just the essentials covered. This one in the *second* paper, though . . ." She paused and shook her head.

"What about it?" Steed asked.

"Well, look at it. It seems all—all—I don't know. All *wrong* somehow. D'you know what I mean?"

Steed picked up the paper and studied the page. "Yes, I do see what you mean," he said at last. "And I think there are two reasons why that particular substitution bothers you. You're absolutely right to be bothered, too—though not more than a half dozen people out of a hundred would notice anything."

"All right, so I pass into the Army Class next term," Emma said with a smile. "Give!"

"First, the kind of story. As you've just pointed out, those other two were typical of the sort of unimportant material that a national daily can put in or leave out as convenient. But in or out, the content of those stories was of *national* interest. The story in this second paper is of extremely *local* interest—a report, for God's sake, of a local council meeting in some village I've never heard of in Leicestershire!"

"And the second?"

"A matter of typography. If you notice—the first two stories match perfectly, so far as the typography is concerned, the rest of the page. The headlines are in the same sort of lettering that the *Courier* would—and does—use. And the type face, the lettering used for body type—that's the type used for the *text* of the stories—is precisely the same as that in all the other stories on the page."

"Yes, I see that. But this other story . . ."

"Doesn't match in the same way. It's not, as they say, in *Courier* style. The body type is completely different, much thicker and heavier; and the headlines are way off, totally out of keeping. The whole effect is much darker and heavier, and you're quite right—it sticks out like a sore thumb. It looks *old-fashioned* beside the rest of the page, don't you think?"

Emma nodded excitedly. "Yes," she said, "you've hit it. That's *exactly* the effect. That's what must have been bothering me!"

Steed was still looking at the story. "I'll tell you something else about this piece," he said thoughtfully. "*It's over a year old!* Look: it quotes this alderman as saying, 'The council hopes the estimate can be approved by the county authority before the Bassetdown by-pass is opened by the Minister of Transport next month'." He dropped the paper back on the table. "The Bassetdown by-pass *was* opened by the Minister of Transport—in July *last year*."

"Bully for Bassetdown," Emma said lightly.

"Indeed. And bully for you, Mrs Peel! This must be the clue we're looking for, the clue they were prepared to kill to stop us finding."

"I still can't see how it helps us."

"Somebody slipped up. Whoever it was that faked up this page, the second time they did it, made a mistake. Instead of carefully using or fabricating a story set in the same types as the *Courier*'s own, he found an old story lying around that had never been used, and—because it happened to fit exactly the hole left by lifting the Carew report to the front page—he bunged it in to save trouble, thinking nobody'd notice."

"And now that we have noticed?"

"It's a direct pointer in some way—it must be!—to how or where the faking's done. Come on . . . we're going back to the flat to see if we can find out!"

A small flat parcel was lying on the mat under the letterbox in Steed's hallway. It was wrapped in white paper and carried two large seals in red wax like an old-fashioned prescription from a chemist's. It was addressed in immaculate copperplate longhand to:

John Steed Esquire,
Number Five Westminster Mews,
London Southwest One.

. . . and it was franked with a small rubber stamp carrying the words *By Hand*. On the back, near the edge of the wrapping paper, a return address was die-stamped rather like that on an old-fashioned letter-head. It read: *Department G, Room 112, Whitehall, S.W.1.*

Emma was entranced. "Isn't that *delightful*!" she cried. "And I do love that Department G bit! Like those ads in the classified sections of sweetshop magazines—How To Slough Off Those Unwanted Inches in Nine Easy Lessons. Send s.a.e. and 4s. 6d. for *free* brochure to Department Q . . . and an address in Willesden. The whole thing implies a huge, busy building full of Departments A to P as well as Q—when in fact it's a dreadful little man who doesn't shave holed up in an attic with no curtains."

Steed grinned. "It's quite prosaic, really," he said. "Though I *am* glad to see it. I asked a friend to send me along a copy of *Hemming's.*"

"And you had to go to Department G just for that?"

"Well, they're expensive. Four guineas—and *we* can't claim exes!"

"You learn more every day, don't you!" Emma said. "Well, open it up then. I can't wait!"

Steed unwrapped the royal blue volume with gold lettering and leafed through until he came to page 65. "Good Lord!" he said. "There's something wrong here. Page 65 is a whole page ad for a duplicating machine!"

"And page 66?"

He turned the leaf over. "A listing of independent news-

agencies in Asia. I'll have to have second opinions, I think.
Coffee and brandy while we wait?"

He removed the remains of the *coq au vin* from the table,
went into the bedroom to make a telephone call, then crossed
the living room and disappeared into the kitchen. A few minutes
later, he reappeared with two delicate tulip glasses a quarter full
of pale brandy, cups and saucers, and an aluminium coffee
percolator of the pattern favoured by French housewives. "It
won't be as nice as the Cona, I'm afraid," he said apologetically,
"but it'll keep us going until Matthew arrives."

"Matthew?"

"Matthew Butler. He's *the* expert on newspaper typography
and press lore generally."

"Steed, you haven't pulled him out of bed on a night like
this? If you had to see him tonight, couldn't we have gone
round to him?"

"Certainly not. It's not twelve o'clock yet. It's stopped raining
—and anyway he'll adore to come. Matthew loves a mystery."

They had finished their second cups of coffee before the
doorbell rang. Matthew Butler had a long, concave nose, a
long upper lip and a wide mouth which together gave him
something of the air of a disapproving duck. He wore horn-
rimmed spectacles and carried a bulging brief case.

He looked at Steed's copy of *Hemming's*, examined the torn
page found in Lindale's hand, and went to fetch his brief case.
He took out a much thumbed copy of the press guide, checked
it against Steed's new one, and then rummaged in the bag again.
Eventually he produced two books in the same format and
colour as *Hemming's*, but much slimmer and in soft instead of
hard covers. He checked the torn page against these, too—
straightening himself with a satisfied grunt when he got to the
second.

"Yes, well, you haven't got all the facts, you see," he said
patronisingly at last. "*Hemming's* publishes a new edition every
year, like most reference books. But it also publishes two
supplements a year—and fortunately I happen to have the
current pair with me. I've been able to check that your torn page
is in fact page 65 of the more recent of these, published only a
few weeks ago."

"And the section it's from?"

"Well, that's interesting in a way. Pages 65 and 66 fall in the section dealing with publications which have—ah—ceased to publish."

"Do you mean the torn page I found in this murdered man's hand is in fact part of a list of papers that have folded?"

"Well, yes. If you like to put it that way."

"I love to put it that way. It means we're getting somewhere!"

"They will all have ceased publication since the *previous* supplement—in the past six months or so, in fact."

Steed carried over the copy of the *Courier* carrying the "wrong" story, which he had purloined from the Foreign Office department they had been in earlier. "You're a splendid chap, Matthew," he said. "Now—tell me if any of the papers which have ceased publication, and are on the list on that piece of torn paper, would have been likely to have had *this* type in stock."

Butler looked at the bogus story, which Steed had ringed in red marker pencil. "Good gracious me," he said. "That's a curious way to see a story set in these days! The headline's in Windsor Elongated, I think—or is it Gloucester Bold Extra Condensed . . . let's have a look at a lower-case N . . . No, the second leg slants *outwards*: it *is* Windsor Elongated; 36-point, I should say . . . And the text, why that's in 8-point Gloucester Bold Condensed. A similar type in a way, but quite a different family. It's Number 198 in the Monotype classification, if you want to know."

"What I want to know much more is this," Steed answered. "Which of those papers that have folded, among those on the list I showed you, would have been likely to have had these two types in stock?"

"Oh, very few, I should think. Very few," Butler said, shaking his head sadly. "Let's have a look at that paper again." He took the crumpled page and smoothed it out on his knee. "Now let's see," he began. "*The Carnwellian*, the *Coronet*, the *Churchman* . . ? No, there's only a couple, Mr Steed, who'd have had those two in stock."

"Which two, Matthew?"

"That agricultural thing published in Exeter, the *Cow Breeder* or something. And a small provincial evening, the Hanningford *Clarion*. It went out of business about six months ago."

"Hanningford? That's in Leicestershire, isn't it?"

"I believe so."

Steed went to a bookcase and came back with a big gazetteer. He flicked through the pages. "Oh, that must be it, definitely," he said after a few minutes. "Look—Hanningford's less than ten miles from the village where that year-old council story came from. You're sure that paper—the *Chronicle* was it?—would have these types in stock?"

"The *Clarion*. Yes, definitely. For some reason they held a quantity of those West Country founts. Even their body type was a Gloucester."

"That does it, then. The Hanningford *Clarion*'s the clue Lindale was trying to give us, the clue our friends with the artillery were trying to prevent us getting."

"But what does it *mean*?" Emma asked. "What does it tell us? How much further on does it get us, Steed?"

"We've been given the clue," the undercover man said. "Now it's up to us to interpret it. And for that, I think, we'll have to take a little trip . . ."

"You can't mean we're going to *Hanningford* tonight?"

"Have you ever been along the M.1. at night?" Steed asked softly.

12

THE PRINTER'S THAT WAS DEAD BUT
WOULDN'T LIE DOWN

EMMA insisted on calling in at her own flat on the way north to
the beginning of the M.1. Steed waited in the Bentley while she
went upstairs, as she said, to change into something more suitable for a *provincial* burglary. She was back in seven and a half
minutes wearing white boots with black stripes up the front,
and a short, mad fur coat whose black-and-white alternating
bands gave her the look of a jaunty young zebra. She tossed
a small hold-all on the back seat of the car and climbed
in.

"That *can't* be a rabbit coat!" Steed exclaimed in astonishment as he let in the clutch and headed the car towards Hendon
and the north.

Emma nodded. "None of the best people would be seen
dead in mink these days," she said coolly. "A good designer
can have just as much fun with rabbit."

"Well, I suppose they were bound to find some alternative
to myxamatosis," Steed said cynically.

Emma curled up inside her coat and went to sleep until they
pulled into the service area at Newport Pagnell for petrol, after
which she took over the wheel.

"I always feel tremendously arrogant sitting here," she said.
"But it does seem a long way from the ground after my little
Lotus!"

"You look tremendously arrogant sitting anywhere, my
dear," Steed said politely. "Do you mind if I snatch a few
minutes sleep, too?"

They made the 100-mile journey in good time. Although the
road was still wet and the spray thrown by heavy lorries travel-
ling north continually fouled the Bentley's upright windscreen,
it still lacked a few minutes to 2 a.m. when Emma braked,
blipped once delicately on the heavy throttle pedal, and slid
the lever into third to nurse the car round the curving slip road

signposted to Hanningford.

The place was a few miles to the east of the motorway, between Market Harborough and Leicester—an uneasy *mélange* of market town, pre-war ribbon development and industrial zone. The building where the Hanningford *Clarion* had been published and printed lay in the middle of the latter region. At the turn of the century, it had no doubt been a busy and prosperous quarter, but the march of progress had passed it by and it lay now derelict and unkempt—a mile and a half of decay straggling northwards between the railway and a canal.

Olympus House was a square, unadorned building in grimy Victorian brick flanked by a furniture depository on one side and a timber yard on the other. The severe façade was pierced only by arched window embrasures and an entrance above which a curving brass plate still faintly announced the name of the paper. Across the road, a light engineering works, a scrapyard and a coal dump bordered the dismal canal. A string of black barges lay moored to the towpath by the dump. Along Canal Street on either side, solid nineteenth century warehouses, offices and disused factories stretched in varying degrees of decrepitude. There wasn't a dwelling to be seen.

The Bentley bumped along the patched and potholed street as Emma sought a discreet parking place. Eventually she turned into a vacant lot half a block beyond the *Clarion* building, stopped the engine and shook Steed awake.

There were no clouds here. The stars glittered coldly in the profundity of the night sky and a cool, moist wind freshened their faces as they picked their way back to the street through a rubble of broken bricks, dismantled iron bedsteads and abandoned motor tyres. In the wan light of Canal Street's widely-spaced lamps, the gloomy frontages frowned ahead and behind.

"One can readily see that a local evening paper might boast only a small circulation here," Emma observed as they approached the sooty front of Olympus House. "I suppose it grew up in the expansion after the industrial revolution, lasted into the era of Edwardian prosperity, then died in the depression and has never really got on to its feet again."

"Most deaths are reasonably final," Steed commented, "though it does seem as though someone's trying to apply a little artificial respiration to the corpse of this paper at least."

"I really meant the whole area—not just the paper."

"Oh. But there are still plenty of people in Hanningford as a whole. It's just that they drive off in their Vauxhalls now to work in Leicester or Market Harborough, rather than walking down here at six o'clock in the morning when the hooter blows."

"'Hanningford as a hole' is good," Emma said. "How are we going to get into this mausoleum?"

"Like a schoolboy from the era of my youth, you're going to keep *cave* here by the door, while I find an alleyway or something and—er—effect an entry from the back."

Between the *Clarion* and the furniture store, a yard about 25 feet wide was roofed over with corrugated iron and closed off from the street by rusty iron gates with barbed wire on top. Steed passed this and walked silently on down the street, while Emma waited—feeling rather like an advertisement for a saucy movie—under the street lamp on the deserted pavement. He passed several buildings, eventually looking over his shoulder, waving once and disappearing up a narrow side road. Ten minutes later, there were surreptitious noises from inside the *Clarion* building. Emma turned to see one of the wooden double doors open. Steed was stading there, beckoning, his small flashlight in one hand.

"Did you have any difficulty?" she asked as he relocked the door behind her.

"Not really. Getting in was easy enough: the trouble was finding a way to the back of the building. In the end, I had to go down·the next side road."

"Yes, I saw you disappearing up there."

"The railway runs along parallel with Canal Street, and this road goes over it on a bridge. I just dropped down on to the embankment and walked back along it until I came to this building again. There's a great siding out at the back there."

Inside the two front doors of the building, a short hallway was bordered with an empty office on either side. A flight of wooden stairs then led around an old-fashioned, hand-operated lift to the upper floors. Beyond the stairs, a heavy door led directly to the machine room. Both front offices were covered in dust, the windows opaque with grime. But the stairs were unexpectedly clean and the editorial rooms on the first floor had a used look. Here, too, the windows were covered in filth and cobwebs—but there were signs of occupation just the same.

The rooms were mostly furnished, the desks and chairs being as free from dust as the floor, and underneath were small pieces of paper, screwed up carbons, bright paper clips and the other detritus of an office, none of which looked as though it was at least six months old.

The stone, too, one floor higher up, appeared equally tenanted. All the cases of type were bright and shining and Steed found two linotype machines whose reservoirs had certainly been filled with molten lead within the past week. On the third floor, the Process department at the top of the stairs was obviously in current use, though the remainder of the rooms were as dusty as the offices at the entrance. The fourth and fifth—which had housed the paper's administrative and accounts offices—had as clearly remained unused for many months.

Down on the ground floor again, they pushed through the heavy door into the machine room. The presses were surprisingly free of dust, and the machines, unsheeted, appeared to be in splendid condition, gleaming and oiled. Steed played the beam of his flashlight over them all.

"You'd never have thought that they even *had* rotaries in a dump like this, would you?" he muttered as he led the way to what had once been the works entrance at the side of the building. There was a small office, rather like a stage-doorkeeper's hutch, with a flapped counter, a rusty machine for punching time cards, and the usual rack hanging on one wall for the cards themselves. Some of the places still held yellowed pieces of pasteboard.

"I wonder what jobs Winstanley, Pope, Gregson, Hetherington and Knockold, J, have now?" Steed ruminated as he flicked through the rack.

"They've either been taken on by the Leicester *Mercury*," Emma said, "or—if they want to earn real money!—they're working as construction navvies on yet another extension to the M.1 . . ."

The scarred wooden door of the works entrance led out into the yard Emma had seen from the street. Beneath the corrugated iron roofing, Steed's torch showed up cobbled setts criss-crossed with the recent marks of many heavy tyres, a line of racks for workers' bicycles, and a row of huge galvanised waste bins. These were about five feet high and six wide.

"I guess they must have had special arrangements for clearing these with the local council," Emma said, wandering over to one of them. "It's positively terrifying, the amount of *paper* we gather in our lives. All of it has to be found a place or thrown away, and either becomes increasingly difficult, the more you have! It must be even worse for newspapers, I should think . . . *Steed! Bring that light here a minute!*"

"What is it? Have you found something?" the undercover man asked as he hurried across with the torch.

"I think so. Yes. This bin's nearly full of paper . . ."

Together they peered over the top of the receptacle as Steed played the beam to and fro. There was used copy paper, typing paper, wrapping paper, there were festoons of punched tele-printer tape and rolls of galley proofs squashed in. But most of all, the bin was full of newsprint.

And from what they could see, the newsprint consisted of dozens and dozens of front pages from the London *Courier* . . .

Steed let his breath out in a long sigh of comprehension. "So that *is* it," he said softly. "I was pretty sure, but this definitely confirms it! Let's have a closer look at this rubbish—and at the paper in the other bins, too."

They dragged out armfuls of the waste paper and carried it back into the building. On the counter of the timekeeper's office, they spread it all out and examined what they had found.

There was nothing among the rubbish but *Courier* front-pages. The discarded pages were from the issues of four dates only.

And the dates tallied with the occasions on which bogus reports of Sir George Carew's speeches had appeared on the Continent.

What must happen, Steed told Emma as they replaced the paper in the bins and then made their way back to the Bentley, was that whole bundles of the first editions destined for the Continent must be hi-jacked from lorries after they left Fleet Street. The bundles must then be unwrapped and the front page / back page folds stripped off—to be replaced by folds carrying the fake speech reports, which it now seemed clear were pre-pared on each occasion in advance at the old *Clarion* works.

"So fine," Emma said briskly. "So now we know how. But we still have to find out who—and, I suppose, why. But for me there are plenty of questions left in the how section without bothering yet about those."

"Naturally," Steed answered. "But fire away: let's have them. It all makes it clearer in one's mind, talking about it. Apart from which you are quite likely to hit on some snag I've overlooked."

"Well, for a start, assuming the substitution is done in the way you've just outlined—and I'm sure it probably is—how can it be done in time for the papers still to arrive on schedule? I mean, this is over a hundred miles from London to begin with, and that's not just a matter of a few minutes here or there."

"I think I can answer that. I do have one fact that you don't!"

"Yes?"

"The *Gazette* and the *Globe* are taken to the Continent from London Airport, like almost all the other nationals and Sundays, by ordinary BEA scheduled flights—which is why the alterations to them have always been much simpler and much milder than those to the *Courier*."

"You mean there isn't enough time to do anything complicated?"

"Exactly. No switching pages about from inside to outside—just a facsimile of the page with one or two paragraphs altered in the relevant story. They don't have to mess around finding substitute stories to fill the hole when they lift a report on the front page. Whatever's done has to be done between Fleet Street and the airport, after all—probably in a van or lorry on the way. But there's only an hour or so to do it in."

"And the *Courier*?"

"The *Courier*'s a different matter. Borridale explained it all to me the other day. Because it's a richer paper with a larger circulation—over five million now, he told me—and because the lord's an incurable show-off anyway, it sends its continental editions out via a small fleet of fast private planes."

"That *is* a bit ostentatious, I admit. There was a rather good little light plane once called an Airspeed Courier—my father had one—I suppose he doesn't use these as a sort of ad?"

"No, I think you can get rather faster ones now! But he would have done, believe me!"

"How do these private freight services work?"

"He has around half a dozen crates, I think. Each one has a flight path taking in several major cities which it visits in turn —either in a straight line or on a round trip. One plane will take papers to Brussels, Amsterdam, Hamburg, Copenhagen, Stockholm and Oslo, for instance; another will drop off bundles at Paris, Strasbourg, Zürich, Munich and Vienna—and a third will do Nice, Turin, Milan, Venice and Rome. And so on."

"That must be why the *Courier* bundles I saw at Schipol were on a different trolley to the others; they'd come on a different aircraft."

"Yes, I'm sure that's it."

"Well, I expect it works quite well. The only disadvantage I can see is that, on any given flight, the farther away a city is, the later it will get its *Couriers*. Whereas the scheduled flights, having a separate plane for each city, virtually, get all their papers more or less at the same time."

"I expect the lord weighed that in the balance against the publicity value and prestige, and found it wanting. But the *Courier*'s scheme has an astonishing advantage for the news-paper fakers."

"What's that?"

"Borridale keeps his little private air force at the airfield at Leicester East."

"But that's only just down the road from here!"

"Exactly, my dear. Take the A.50 to Wigston Magna, turn right and head for Oadby, and it's just down the lane. Perhaps six miles in all."

"Yes," Emma said slowly. "I see what you mean. If the bundles are *supposed* to come in vans from London to Leicester East—"

"They are."

"—then the forgers have all the time it takes to drive up the M.1 to get the papers as printed ready for the substitution: they could have the bundles unwrapped and stripped of their outside folds in plenty of time. But there's one thing I cannot under-stand: the *whole* consignment, surely is destined for the Continent?"

"Yes, it is."

"Then I fail to see how any hi-jack could work. If only *some* of the papers sold abroad had been tampered with, it could be explained, say, by a crooked checker—saying the right number of bundles had been present when in fact some had been taken by the fakers. Perhaps to be put back secretly later. But you couldn't miss it if *the whole lot* were pinched and sent up in another van—I mean somebody'd notice!"

"Perhaps somebody does."

"You mean the actual van crew or crews on the *Courier* staff must be in on it?"

"I'm afraid it looks like it; there's no escaping it," Steed said seriously. "And that would tie in, too, with the murder of Lindale. We know there must have been staff members implicated in that."

"But the whole staff can't be in on it! And yet, to explain everything, it looks as though the whole staff *must* be in on it . . . It doesn't make sense, Steed—for if the *Courier* did want to do this *as a paper*, if it was a concerted effort, they could just print the fake stuff on their own presses without all this elaborate flummery of changing pages and so on."

"No newspaper could get away with openly printing news it knew to be false," Steed said. "But you're right in principle, of course. If the management of the *Courier* wanted for some reason to damage the image of the country—if Borridale aspired to the premiership, for example—they could find plenty of ways less clumsy and less complicated than this."

"So you don't think that's it?"

"I don't think the forgeries—or the motive for them, which is undoubtedly political, either internally or internationally— are in any way the responsibility of the *Courier* as an organ."

"I've one more query in the how section," Emma said.

"Yes?"

"A question of noise. Doesn't anyone hear the presses roaring away in the old *Clarion* building when the substitute front pages are run?"

"It's not too much of a problem for them, if you think of it. Either a 'front' has leased the works and uses them for legitimate print jobs—just slipping in the forgeries on the side when they arise. Or the place is being used clandestinely, without permission. In the first case, any noise would pass without comment, since they'd be printing anyway. And even in the second, I don't think a soul would query it. There's an engineering works opposite and a timber yard next door, both of them likely to make a din. Then, the printing is going to be done mainly in the afternoon, while their din's at its height. And anyway there are no flats or houses near, a furniture store on the other side, railway sidings at the back and a canal across the road—an ideal enough situation for unusual noises *not* to be noticed!"

"I could do a bit of research later on and find out if the works have been leased to any firm recently—and, if so, who they are," Emma said.

"Bless you. I was hoping I could count on you for that. And while you're at it, perhaps one could ask a few questions among the workers around—have they heard anything unusual, seen any identifiable lorries outside the *Clarion* works, and so on? Anything that would point to a direct lead—anything likely to lead us to our clients . . ."

"Yes, I get the general idea," Emma said coldly. "Perhaps it would save you petrol if I just stayed here and waited until they all came on duty at seven thirty."

Steed grinned. "We have to climb this fence, I'm afraid," he said. "Here, let me give you a leg up."

A feeble light wavered towards them as they jumped down into the side road leading to Canal Street. It was an elderly workman on a bicycle pedalling laboriously up the short rise leading to the railway bridge. He stared at Steed's bowler, pin-stripe and umbrella, and at Emma's rabbit coat and white boots. As they passed, he dismounted slowly and stood, holding the handlebars of his machine, looking after them. When they were about ten yards away, he spat noisily into the road.

Opposite the vacant lot where they had left the Bentley, mist lay like smoke in the trough of the canal and wreathed in slow layers among the humped piles of coal in the yard. The water was the colour of lichen. Above, bars of paler green streaked the sky and converged on a clear patch of sulphurous yellow tinged with pink to the east. The dawn was about to break on Hanningford.

"One of King Oliver's masterpieces was called *Canal Street Blues*," Emma said reflectively. "I see what he meant."

13

A MYSTERY BY WIRE!

THE subdued alto chimes of the Swiss repeater Steed wore on his wrist awoke him at midday. He lay for a moment staring at the beams in the ceiling of the unfamiliar room. Sunlight slanted in through the gap between the tapestry curtains and the wooden-ringed pole from which they hung, scalloping a pattern on the wall. Outside, unexpectedly, instead of the noise of traffic, the sound of leisurely footsteps and the conversation of many people hung in the warm air. Then he remembered: it was Sunday morning.

They had arrived in Hanningford's old market square as the sun rose, and had pessimistically tried the front door of a timbered building announcing itself as the Queen's Hotel. To their surprise, the place had been open—and not only was there a night porter awake and friendly, but he had fed them whisky, made them excellent coffee and sandwiches, put the Bentley in the coach yard behind the inn and found them two rooms!

Steed rose and looked down into the square from his window. In the pale light of dawn it had been a litter of papers, straw, animal dung and the splintered remnants of crates and boxes from the Saturday market. All this had been cleared away during the morning and the square was filled now with home-going churchgoers from the Victorian Gothic anachronism in the corner opposite the hotel. The bar was raucous with the clamour of midland farmers when he came downstairs a half hour later—shaved, showered and dressed in a high-buttoned tweed suit in Lovat green which he had thoughtfully packed in a small overnight case before they left.

Mrs Peel had gone out earlier, the receptionist told him, and had left a message that he was not to wait lunch for her. She would be back as soon as she could.

Steed wandered into the crowded dining room and discovered

131

that he would have to wait almost an hour for a table. He decided to spend the time sounding out local opinion in the bar. Few of the men in from the country with whom he struck up conversations, however, knew anything of Hanningford's industrial problem—or even if there was one. "Canal Street?" one of them said. "Oh, yes—that's where Charles Quinnell's timber yard is, isn't it? Dreadful bloody dump, if you ask me. No wonder Charles keeps his office up here in the square!" "The *Clarion*?" another remarked. "Oh, it was too, you know, too blasted local. Church fêtes and committee meetings reported, speeches at the school prizegiving repeated in full— that sort of thing. That's fine if you have a community working *as* a community. But Hanningford today . . . why it's just a dormitory for Leicester or Harborough. People are only interested to read that sort of thing if they have taken part themselves, aren't they? It's no use when half the population have all their interests *outside* the town . . ."

"It was doomed as soon as they built the M.1, anyway," a friend standing near butted in. "Once you can get the London evenings here within a couple of hours of being printed—that's it!"

It was not until he struck up an acquaintance with a fresh-faced young man with spiky hair who worked at a garage on the outskirts of town that Steed could draw any opinion of the area itself.

"Biddlestown, that'd be," the young man said. "That's what they call it around here, Biddlestown. Between the railway and the canal . . . Too old-fashioned for what they call an industrial estate, but there's still a few firms has their places down there. You wouldn't catch me working there, though. Not on your nelly!"

"Why not?" Steed asked. "Is it so dreadful?"

"It's not just dreadful, mate. It's dead. Dead and gone. When they tore off the last page of the 1899 calendar, they should've torn Biddlestown off with it and flushed it down the drain . . ."

"Why d'you dislike it so much?"

"I dunno. The *atmosphere*, I suppose—it's all empty offices, dumps, scrap heaps, old factories. None of it any use any more. No cinema, no dance hall, no houses or flats, not a garage even. Just this ropey old road and the canal. Gives you the creeps."

"D'you think nothing's any good if it's not productive, then?

Or is it that you don't like old things? Or places where people have made money?"

"No, it's not exactly that." The young man considered deeply for a moment. "Look—take cars. You've got a mini; you don't find yourself having it in for the man with a Ferrari or an Alfa. That's class machinery, that is. You may envy him or even admire him—but you're not *contemptuous*. But you take a man with some old pre-war wreck of what may *once* have been a good car, a Bentley or something—despite the name, your mini, cheap as it is, can out-perform, out-corner that old wreck any time. And it's a much better designed, more reliable job altogether—yet this guy puts on *airs* about his ruddy museum piece —D'you know what I mean?"

"Yes," Steed said gravely. "Yes, I know *exactly* what you mean."

"Well that's sort of how I feel about Biddlestown. Contemptuous. You've had your day, Jack. Now move over. Don't stand there expecting pity from *us*—or cheers for what you once were. Here, I'm talking a lot of cock. What'll you have, mate?"

"I'll have another beer, thanks," Steed said. "What do you think's going to happen to this place then?"

"I don't think: I know," the boy said, scraping the moisture from the bottom of the glasses on the bar and handing one to Steed. "Cheers! No—I overheard something the other day at the garage. I was filling up a great black Mercedes—the pump attendant was away a minute, see, it's not really my job, you know—and I heard this big man say to this other guy about how it would be easier when the deal for the *Clarion* works went through—the *Clarion* used to be the local rag, you know. The building's still down in the area you're talking about. Anyway, this other fellow said yes, once the government had changed, they would use the vacant lot nearby and the coal yard and the timber place and make a kind of parade ground, I think he said—and then the first man said, yes, but they'd have to build gradually at first . . . and that was all I heard."

"And what do you think that meant?"

"Well, it's obvious, isn't it? After the election—though that's not until after next summer, of course—they're going to pull all that old dross down and modernise the place . . . new buildings . . . big parks for the cars. The lot. That'll be something like, eh?"

"Yes," said Steed, nodding slowly. "It may have meant that."

Later, he was sitting over lunch when Emma made a fairly spectacular entrance to the dining room in a white trouser-suit piped with black, and a sleeveless black halter-neck sweater which clung to her supple body provocatively as she moved. On her head she wore a black and white beret made in concentric circles like a target.

"Come on in: the waiter's fine!" Steed called into the silence. "And I recommend the saddle of lamb—it's quite delicious. They can offer a tolerable London-bottled Moulin-à-Vent, too."

"My apologies for being late, Steed," Emma said as she settled herself at the table. "You got my message, I hope?"

"In common with every other male in the room, thank you. I am lost in admiration at the infinite capacity of your overnight bag."

"The trick is to keep to one basic colour scheme. Thank you," Emma continued as the waiter handed her a menu.

"Were your researches—valuable?" Steed asked.

"Useful rather than valuable, I'd say, being negative in the main. First, the works have not been leased to anyone since the paper folded—so any printing done there *is* done clandestinely. Secondly, the place *is* up for sale, but nobody has bought it yet. And, finally, there *is* somebody—or some organisation, to be more exact—very interested. But only if they can buy the timber yard adjoining and one or two other lots nearby as well. So no deal's been closed there either. Not much for a morning's work—but you try getting information in an English country town on a Sunday!"

"Things begin to figure, as our transatlantic cousins say," Steed mused. "That fits rather well with a strange rumour I heard from a man in the bar." He related the conversation he had had with the young man from the garage, adding: "I don't suppose you could glean any clue to the organisation interested in buying up half Canal Street?"

"No. I don't think my source knew herself."

"Pity—for I have a pretty good idea that when we find out who it is, we shall be very close to discovering who's pulling this newspaper lark . . . and I wouldn't mind having a glimpse of our friends in the Mercedes either!"

"If we're going back to the *Clarion* this afternoon," Emma said, "I'd better go upstairs and get my things ready."

"I wouldn't do that, my dear. We may find we need to stay here another night," Steed said.

Afterwards, when he had brought the Bentley round to the front of the hotel from the coach-house and was waiting for Emma with the engine ticking over quietly, the young man from the garage emerged from the front door and stopped dead. "I *say*," he breathed in awestruck tones, moving slowly forward as the great car's brightwork struck beams of reflected sunlight from his tiepin, "what a beauty!"

Steed smiled at him in the apprehensive way of the connoisseur who cringes from uninformed praise.

The young man walked all the way round the Bentley twice, cocking his head first to one side and then to the other, examining minutely every detail from the oiled leather bonnet straps to the chain which guarded the enormous petrol filler cap. "Is it an M.G.?" he asked at length.

"No," Steed replied truthfully as Emma ran down the steps and climbed into the passenger seat, "it's not an M.G."

"I bet she goes like a bomb!" the young man said admiringly.

"Well, no," Steed said again. "Not *exactly* like a bomb. More like some pre-war wreck of a Bentley or something . . ."

The young man had the grace to blush as they drove away.

When they got back to Biddlestown, it looked more desolate than ever. Canal Street on a sunny Sunday afternoon and Canal Street in the middle of the night had nothing to choose between them when it came to derelict squalor. On the bank by the barges two men sat somnolently dipping lines into the stagnant water. Their bicycles leaned against the wooden fencing of the coal dump. A quarter of a mile up the street, a handful of children from a Victorian tenement played on the dusty pavement in the sun. A few more scrambled, shouting, among the bricks on the vacant lot where they had left the car during the night. Otherwise, apart from a battered Chevrolet by the entrance to the timber yard, the street was deserted.

Steed parked the Bentley directly outside the *Clarion* building. "We'll go straight in at the front door," he said. " I took the trouble to leave it unlocked. If anyone did wonder, we could be prospective clients who'd got the keys from the agent and had permission to look the place over."

Sooty though the windows were, the difference between searching in daylight and by the narrow beam of a flashlight was tremendous—and they found a clue to the people using the works almost at once.

"It seems obvious that, whenever they use this place, they tidy away every sign of their visit," Emma was saying. "The waste paper baskets are emptied, the proofs are put outside, even the typing paper and pencils are taken away."

Steed was on his knees under a desk. "There's always something they miss, though," he said. "As I missed this last night. Look!"

He backed out and rose to his feet, holding out a metal waste paper basket. At some time or other somebody had spilled sweet tea inside the receptacle. This had evaporated to a sticky ring— and on to the sticky ring a piece of newsprint had stuck, so that when last the bin had been upended and emptied, this had remained behind unnoticed. Steed picked the piece of paper out and held it up to the light.

It was a proof, run off on a spare piece of newsprint for convenience, of a leaflet. Three lines of italic display type ran across the top. They read:

BEAT BACK THE BLACKS!

JOIN THE ANTI-JEWS!

FLING OUT ALL FOREIGNERS!

Below, overprinted across an enormous letter B in a pale tint, several lines of type announced a meeting at an open air site in north London for the previous Wednesday, gave the names of several speakers, and added that there would be "a silver collection for Party Funds." Large, bold lettering across the foot of the page exhorted:

WE FIGHT! — TO WIN BACK BRITAIN FOR THE BRITISH!!

"What's all that in aid of?" Emma asked.

"The Brotherhood," Steed replied sombrely. "That's what the big letter B underlying the information stands for. That's the only identification they ever give. The Special Branch'll be awfully glad to see this—they've wondered for ages where their literature is printed. It never carries an imprint, though it's required to do so by law."

"Who are The Brotherhood, though? Sounds like some kind of secret society."

"It is, in a way. At least it appeals to the little boy who likes secret societies in all of us. It's in fact a highly racialist, neo-fascist party which is seeking an entry into politics in this country."

"Is it strong?"

"Not in numbers. Not yet. But it's being watched with some concern. There've been plenty more of these crackpot little groups, of course—Socialist Action, the British Alliance of Fascists, the National Radical Party and so on. None of them have meant a damn, numerically. And to proscribe them is to grant their wish for publicity. But this one seems to be a little different—unfortunately."

"How do you mean?"

"Well, it's thought to have much stronger backing, financially, for a start. And, unlike the others, it's not run by a small man, a failure for whom this is the only way of making a mark. The brains behind it are cool, ruthless and very shrewd, according to the Special Branch boys."

"You mean it has a particular purpose, other than advancing the claims to fame of its leader?"

"Exactly. The Brotherhood is seeking an entry into politics, as I said. But not with a town councillor here and a parliamentary candidate who loses his deposit there. They're too clever for that. The brains are holding back until, when they do put up candidates, they can be sure of making a bit of a mark—nothing sensational, but a few councils swung, a handful of M.P.'s actually in, much as the brownshirts did in Germany. And until they give the word, of course, the indoctrination proceeds apace."

"They're recruiting a semi-secret following, in fact, to be revealed—or unmasked—when it's most effective? And in the meantime working hard to increase that following?"

"That's it, exactly. Using all the old chauvinistic tricks that appeal so much to weaklings—the master race bit, the idea that you'd be much better off if you hadn't been cheated out of rightful deserts by all those foreigners, the juvenile rhetoric as exampled by the three subtle appeals at the top of this leaflet: beat back the blacks, join the anti-Jews and fling out foreigners! Once that's happened, among the few tiny men left, you can be king! And of course it appeals to the corner-boy types—sloshing BBB and JAJ and FOF in white paint all over the railway bridges at night . . ."

"Who *is* the leader?" Emma asked.

"There isn't one, in the sense of a figurehead—they run an all for one and one for all line. Thus the *Brotherhood*. But there must be one in fact, though nobody has identified him yet. Perhaps we're about to do it now!"

"You're sure it's this group that's behind the newspaper faking?"

"Practically certain, my dear. They're known to be very strong in London, of course, and also in Birmingham, Leeds, Smethwick, Coventry . . . and Leicester. But there are other reasons too."

"You mean if it *wasn't* them, whoever it was would hardly bother to take in outside printing jobs at a works he wasn't entitled to use?"

"Yes. And because, if it is them, it answers conveniently so many problems which have seemed unanswerable. The matter of size, for one."

"Size?"

"The size of the organisation needed to do this. As everybody's constantly reminded us, if this *was* to be done, an awful lot of people would have had to be involved. Well—it *is* done. But we've never really considered this: perhaps an awful lot of people *are* involved!

"We've been put off because we've thought of an awful lot of *disparate* people, a large number of separate individuals stratified by profession, by class, by social activity—and, as young Lindale pointed out, it was unlikely that any such wide cross-section could successfully be recruited for such a scheme. There is, however, one unifying factor which could weld such a diverse group together: a political party, especially if it is a clandestine one."

"There's another problem it would answer," Emma said. "The problem of the hi-jacking. If the vanmen—or even some of them working together in crews—were members of The Brotherhood, this would mean that the papers needn't be hi-jacked at all. They could be worked on in the *Courier*'s own vans—rather like post office sorting!—on their way north. And a crooked man making up schedules could easily write in the journey as a half hour longer than it actually is, to give the vans time to make a detour via Canal Street and have the new front pages put on."

"You're right," Steed said. "Similarly, the organisation could have infiltrated men into key positions in London Airport Traffic—or seduced men already there—to bend schedules a little to allow time for the other two papers to be altered. And they'd have to have people in employment at foreign airports to see to things there, and others outposted on the editorial floors of the papers involved to handle detail matters of timing required for the successful operation of the scheme."

"Well, I really cannot see—" Emma began. She broke off suddenly.

A sudden electric whining broke the dusty afternoon silence in the close air of the office.

It was followed a few seconds later by a click, a light chuntering noise, and then the heavy clatter of a teleprinter.

The noise came from the adjoining office. They hurried through to see what was happening. Among a collection of filing cabinets, chairs and cupboards pushed into a corner, a machine in an ancient oak case was chattering away. As they watched, the carriage slammed back to the right and the teleprinter spewed out paper until the wording was clear of the perspex window which closed off the top of the machine. Steed tore the wide paper off against the bevelled edge of the slit in the perspex through which it emerged. There were three lines of lettering on it:

1546 - - - 0908 ALLO ERE LDN CALLG M'CHSTR. PREPARG TO TROXXXXX TRANSMIT EDITION 0908 FOR1008. ARE U REWXXXX READY QUERY.........

1547.0908 MCR TO LDN. ALLO YES T'KS READY. CARRY ON.........

"Good Lord!" Steed said softly. "D'you know what this is?"

"Other than that it's a conversation between an operator in Manchester and another in London, no. Except that the Manchester man's a much better operator: he's made no mistakes, whereas the other has mis-fingered twice and forgotten to operate his space bar between two groups on the second line."

The teleprinter had begun to print again.

"Quite true. But the important part is, who's sending the messages—and I believe this printer here's a leak machine from the direct line connecting the *Courier*'s offices in London and Manchester," Steed said.

"What's a leak machine?"

"Well, you know you can either teleprint direct, on a keyboard rather like a typewriter's, or punch codes on a perforated tape and feed it through later—well, in each case the electrical impulses produced travel down a direct line leased from the GPO and recreate what you've just done at the other end. In other words it's like typewriting by remote control—only it's two-way: if it's a transmitting machine, you can answer back."

"Understood."

"Right. Well you can hitch up as many teleprinters as you like —you just plug them in like electric fires—to a given source. And whatever that source transmits will come up on all of them. A leak machine is merely a tap taken from that line: it shows you anything sent either way, but you can't yourself join in the conversation."

"What happens between the *Courier*'s Manchester and London offices then?"

"The *Courier*, like many other papers, prints its northern editions separately at Manchester. But rather than carry an entire editorial staff duplicated at the Manchester office, everything except the material slanted for the north itself is printed exactly as in London on teleprinted instructions from the head office. The typographical details, the headlines, the copy as sub-edited, the dimensions, the captions for the pictures—everything is sent on the machine. And if Manchester have any queries, they can ask them right back on the machine!"

"What about the pictures themselves?"

"Those they know about, they send in advance or order in duplicate from agencies. Urgent ones they send by wire. I suppose they do the same thing for any pictures on the fake front pages they print here."

They picked up the paper as it was fed out of the slit, and read the details of the next day's *Courier*. "We'd better not tear off any more," Steed said, "or they might notice when they come in."

The paper around the carriage in the machine jerked from side to side, unrolled line by line, and concertina-ed into an untidy heap behind the case.

"What I cannot understand," Steed said, "is why? I happen to know that Carew's spending the weekend with the P.M. at Chequers. He's definitely not making any speeches. Yet presumably they must be about to fake another substitution, or this machine wouldn't go: I'm sure it doesn't record the London-Manchester traffic *unless* there's dirty work afoot."

The teleprinter stopped, whined, and then began again faster than before.

ALLO ERE LDN 2 - - it began - - SPL. FOR HANNINGFD 090'XXXX 0908 FOR 100'XXX XXXXXXX

ALLO ERE LDN 2. SPL. FOR HANNINGFD 0908 FOR 1008 PAGE ONE LEAD TAKE ONE BEGINS. 5 COL BANNER 4 COL 4 COL 144 PT GILL SANS BLD COND TITLING 525 FIRST LINE QUOTE SIR GEORGE WAS SECOND LINE RIGHT UNQUOTE SAYS THIRD LINE PREMIER . . .

"This is most interesting," Steed said. "This means they have a transmitting machine wherever the leak comes from in London —this is someone actually sending instructions for the fake story. Somebody not very experienced at teleprinting, judging by the copy here!"

Together they watched the structure of the bogus story emerge.

"Do you understand?" Steed asked. "No? — Well London 2 is obviously the identification mark of whoever gives orders for the faking. Today's paper—that's to say the one printed today for reading tomorrow—is called Sunday-for-Monday in newspaper parlance. Or, if you do it by dates, August-9-for-August-10. They ask for a three line heading across five columns, four columns and four columns, in a type called Gill Sans Bold Condensed Titling, whose Monotype classification number is 525. They want it in the 144 point size—that's two inches deep! —and it will read in its three lines: 'SIR GEORGE WAS RIGHT' SAYS PREMIER . . .'"

The text, when it began to come through, purported to be a report quoting the Premier at a specially called press conference, at which he completely underwrote everything the

Foreign Secretary had said in the four previous bogus speeches
—and added a few remarks of his own for good measure.

"Good grief, this is dynamite!" Steed exclaimed. "They're
getting bolder and bolder. Yesterday's effort had at least this
in common with truth—that Carew had *made* a speech, even
though no papers reported it. And that was the first time they
'lifted' a non-existent story to the front page . . . But now it's
come to non-existent *speeches*; it's a total fabrication altogether.
It's got to be stopped."

"Splendid," Emma said. "How?"

"Follow up the only lead we have. I must get back to Town
as soon as possible and identify the tap—the place from which
this machine leaks its material—and see from whose office in
the *Courier* it emanates. Once we know who it is, we'll try and
tie it in with The Brotherhood—but there's not a moment to
lose if we're to uncover the whole plot before the fake front
pages are printed here and substituted for those going to the
Continent."

"What time is it now? How long have you got? How can
I help?"

"It's almost four fifteen. We have until the middle of the
evening before the five-star is ready to leave the *Courier* building; a few hours more before the planes take off from Leicester
East with the continental deliveries—and we'd better get the
hell out of here now: there'll be staff coming in privily at any
moment to carry out these teleprinted instructions and get the
ball rolling . . ."

Outside the *Clarion* works, Steed handed Emma into the
Bentley and roared off down Canal Street towards the centre
of the town. "I'd like you to stay here and keep an eye on the
Clarion," he said. "Base yourself on the Queen's Hotel—it's a
good thing we didn't check out—hire a taxi and come down
here every hour or so to reconnoitre. Give me two hours to
reach London, and I'll ring you at the hotel for progress reports
every hour after that . . ."

He left her at the corner of the market square and, with a
debonair wave of his hand, pointed the car's aristocratic nose
towards the south-west and thundered off into the sun.

14

A TURN FOR THE WORSE

STEED could not tell definitely whether or not the Mercedes was following him until after he had driven on to the M.1 at Lutterworth. He had been aware—as would have been any good driver—that among the cars in his rear view mirror as he sped south down the A.50 was a large black saloon. But it was only as he neared Husband's Bosworth that the German car closed up enough for him to distinguish the details. It was a 300 S.E., the biggest of the fuel-injection models, and there seemed to be about six people in it as far as he could see from the restricted view afforded by the glass. Both the driver and the man sitting next to him were anonymous behind large sunglasses.

It followed him through the town and was close behind when he made the right hand turn on to A.4114. Even so, the undercover man might have noticed nothing: there must, after all, have been plenty of people from Hanningford and Market Harborough heading for the motorway along the same route. But a sticking carburetter needle was causing the Bentley to overheat through too weak a mixture, and Steed was forced to stop just before Kilworth, at the approach to the M.1, to free it.

As soon as he had set off again with the trouble rectified, he looked into the mirror again. And the black Mercedes was still there, exactly as before.

After that he was suspicious—but still not sure. It was perfectly possible that they had been observed leaving the *Clarion* works: dare he spend the necessary time to confirm this?

He decided that he must, and drove on to the north-bound carriageway of the motorway at Lutterworth. The black saloon followed suit.

Ten miles nearer Leicester, Steed slowed as the white-on-blue signs warned of the approach to a service area. He swung the car out of the slow lane, dropped into second to negotiate the petrol station, drove through the parking space and past the

143

restaurant and maintenance area to the bridge, crossed this, and then wound round and down in a tight curve to rejoin the motorway on the southbound carriageway.

The Mercedes was still behind him.

That settled it, then. He was being followed. Steed smiled grimly to himself and took the needle of the Bentley's tachometer up into the red segment at the bottom right hand section of the dial. The urbane contralto of the close-ratio gearbox rose to a howl and then a scream.

Steed double-declutched into third. The needle dropped back, then rose rapidly again as he pressed the throttle pedal remorselessly towards the footboard. Once more the precision-cut steel cogs screamed as the white pointer moved from black to red on the dial.

The agent eased the short, heavy lever with its large spherical knob into top.

He pulled over to his right to pass a light van and put his foot down again. The needle on the matched speedometer dial swung swiftly across from 75 to 80, from 80 to 85 ... At ninety miles an hour, the 35-year-old thoroughbred rode the hot concrete as steadily as a modern grand prix car. The deep exhaust note bellowed back from the large-bore tailpipe, the roar from the carburetter air intakes blended with the full-throated sound of the engine itself and the more discreet whine of top gear. The huge tyres sucked noisily at the road—and over everything thundered the buffeting of the wind.

The Bentley's upright windscreen created a turbulence at this speed which resulted in a dead area directly behind it—so the hair on the top of Steed's head, which was higher than the top rail of the screen, astonishingly remained almost completely unruffled. A back draught plucked at his shoulders, however, and heaved at the black mohair tonneau cover which shrouded all the seats but his own.

Traffic was fairly light. There were no heavy lorries and the majority of the cars were cruising steadily in the sixties or seventies, their occupants probably enjoying the rolling, wooded countryside in the late afternoon sun. Steed glanced at the small rectangle of glass mounted just above the dashboard. The Mercedes was maintaining its position, about three hundred yards behind.

Steed pressed his foot down farther still. The blown 4½-litre could still exceed the 100 miles per hour mark. Over the high, arched bonnet and the slender, raked wings with their polished sidelamps, the winged mascot above the radiator cap arrowed its way down the dual ribbon of the motorway towards London and the south. The roar of the engine, the snarl of the exhaust, the shriek of supercharger, gearbox and wind, all blended into a single exhilarating noise as the very air seemed to part before the Bentley with a sound like the splitting of an immense sheet of calico, sucking the car irresistibly forward into the tear.

A slight smile played about the corners of the British agent's mouth as he drove. His hands, lean, sensitive and light-fingered on the wheel, nursed the machine over every undulation in the surface, through every gust of wind from the side, as the speed-ometer needle crept slowly towards the 100. Steed was enjoying himself.

They had just passed a knot of slower moving traffic and pulled in to the nearside lane again when he glanced once more at the rear-view mirror. The black car seemed to have gained a little. He coaxed the last ounce of power from the Bentley. The motorway stretched ahead—deserted now for as far as he could see, an empty pathway laid down across a great swell of country. The needle flickered on to the third division between the figures 100 and 105. He looked yet again at the glass. The pursuer was even nearer. Somebody seemed to be leaning out of the offside window.

And then abruptly the squat shape of the Mercedes, with its wide radiator shell and bulging sides, vanished; disintegrated in a shower of fragmented glass. Something stung Steed on the cheek. The Bentley swerved momentarily, veered across the carriageway to the fast lane, clipped the dried turf beyond the white margin-line of the central strip, raising a small puff of dust, and was brought gradually to heel and so back to the inside lane.

For a moment Steed didn't know what had happened—he was too busy driving the car to pay much attention at that speed. Then a spider's web of cracks starred his laminated glass wind-screen. There was a hole the size of a half crown where they all converged. He flicked his eyes down to the driving mirror—and saw nothing but a brass backing plate with a ragged tear punched in it. A fragment of silvered glass dislodged itself from the twisted frame and fell to the floor as he watched.

Then he realised. They were shooting at him from the other car.

The first bullet must have shattered the mirror as he was looking into it. Another had gone through his windscreen. Others, perhaps, had buried themselves in the upholstery, were already draining fuel from a holed tank . . .

You never realise how much you use—and rely on—a rear view mirror until you haven't got one. As any man will know whose wife has turned the glass to the passenger side to powder her nose—and omitted to turn it back. The effect, on glancing automatically up and finding, instead of the expected, orderly section of road with advancing traffic, a distorted vision of houses or trees speeding past in the wrong direction, is much like a douche of cold water. And Steed, finding himself now suddenly bereft of the means of keeping his enemy in view, felt much the same sense of shock and deprivation.

The Bentley's maximum, absolute top weight, was 104 m.p.h. And he was already doing virtually that. The three-litre engine of the modern Mercedes could probably push the two ton saloon up to ten miles an hour faster than that. Apart from which the fuel-injection car would have better brakes and a much lower centre of gravity. And it was—he permitted himself a fleeting glance over his shoulder—less than a hundred yards behind him and still gaining. The road ahead was still clear.

He began to weave the Bentley from side to side of the carriageway in a series of controlled swerves. This would effectively reduce his maximum speed but it would have two advantages: if the heavy saloon tried to follow him through the curves, its softer springing and heavier, more overhung body would build up a progressive weight transference making it ever more difficult to change direction accurately, finally perhaps inducing an oversteer so pronounced that the car would either lose adhesion and spin or be forced to reduce speed drastically: and if the driver of the Merc was too wily a bird for that one and merely drove ahead in a straight line—well, at least it had the merit of making Steed himself a much harder target to hit!

He snatched another backward glance. The German car was maintaining an absolutely straight course in the centre lane. There appeared to be several people leaning out of the windows. He saw the puff of smoke from a gun in the instant that he looked and a moment later a second network of lines appeared on the Bentley's windscreen. Just afterwards a rip manifested itself in the tonneau cover over the passenger seat.

Steed put one hand up to his cheek. It came away with the fingers stained red. He could feel the warm blood trickling down skin chilled by the rush of wind to his jawbone. A splinter of glass must have flown up and nicked him when the mirror was hit.

But this wasn't good enough, the undercover man felt. He had a lighter, slower car. His opponents outnumbered him considerably and were heavily armed. In addition, they were in a position to use their weapons while he couldn't hit back.

If he remained on the motorway, he would be a sitting duck: it would only be a matter of time before one of the bullets hit him or punctured a tyre.

They were fast overhauling a small knot of vehicles which had come into sight just beyond the top of a rise in the downs. Three small family cars were passing a motor caravan and a lorry laden with market produce. The Bentley and the Mercedes roared past both groups in close convoy—and Steed noticed, just as they were about to pull in again, the giant sign on the hard shoulder: NORTHAMPTON 5000.

If he could manage to stay alive for three miles, he might have a chance . . .

He kept the car at the round ton for a few hundred yards and then, as more southbound traffic hove into sight, pulled in behind a convoy of three minis coasting along at about 75. He figured that the occupants of the Mercedes would hardly dare shoot at him in public in front of witnesses—and he was right. The German car slowed and fell in about two hundred yards behind him.

The 4000, the 3000, the 2000 and then the 1000 warning signs for Northampton came up on their left. Here, Steed felt was one point where he might have a go. If he could tempt the black saloon to overshoot the slip road, while taking it himself, it might be miles before they could find a crossover to bring them back on the northern carriageway. He'd have a shot, anyway.

None of the three minis was exhibiting a flashing indicator, so he presumed they were all going straight on in the direction of London. About four hundred yards from the Northampton slip road, he suddenly slammed the Bentley into third and pulled out to pass the last one.

The Mercedes growled in pursuit.

Two hundred yards from the slip road, he forged slowly ahead of the middle mini, the German car sitting close on his tail. But instead of going on to pass the front mini, Steed flicked on his left-hand indicator, blared his horn and swung the Bentley's wheel over to the left, cutting in between the two leading minis and carving up the second one, as he told Emma afterwards, something shocking! The driver of the little saloon braked violently, hooted and waved his fist as Steed hurtled across his bows and rocketed up the slip road.

As he had hoped, the manœuvre took the Mercedes driver by surprise. Since Steed had waited until the very last moment, the driver of the pursuing car would have had to have followed him as though on rails to have made the turn—but his way was blocked by the last two minis, and although he braked fiercely, by the time he could have swung across behind the last one, the car's momentum had already carried it beyond the slip road.

Steed laughed aloud. "Sorry, mate!" he apostrophised the justly enraged driver of the mini. "Naughty thing to do—but needs must when the devil drives. And today he's at the wheel of a 300 S.E."

He turned right off the slip road, crossed the motorway by the bridge, and headed southwest for Towcester and Brackley; but he had reckoned without the daring and initiative of the Mercedes driver. As soon as he realised he had been outwitted, he trod on everything and slowed the big car down to 40, executing a U-turn across the central strip with tyres screaming. It bumped over the baked earth and demolished some geraniums, to jolt back on to the fast lane of the northbound carriageway on the other side. There was obviously no such formality as obeying the regulations for the people in the Mercedes . . . Then, blandly ignoring the flashing lights, the hoots and the shouts of wrath, the big car pulled right across to the near side, taking the slip road for Northampton from *that* carriageway. It was coming up the hill to the bridge just as Steed flashed past from the other side. The driver shrugged his shoulders, turned right and fell in behind as before.

Steed knew the by-roads around here from holidays when he was a child. He twisted and turned, dived down narrow lanes between tall hedgerows, dipped around right-angled bends under railway bridges, plunged into small, steep valleys brimming with trees, dashed up hills to clatter across the yards of farms— and all to no avail, for the Mercedes, however much he might gain on it momentarily, refused to be shaken off . . .

At one point, rounding a sharp bend at the bottom of a dip in the road, he thought he might have made it: over the top of the banked hedgerow, from his high vantage point in the driving seat of the Bentley, he could look across the apex of the curve to where the lane passed the entrance to a cornfield—and he could see a tractor hauling a load of straw just about to emerge from the gateway. The driver of the Mercedes, from his lower position, would have been able to see nothing but the lush banks of the lane itself.

Steed changed into second and put his foot down. As the car surged forwards at the corner, he swung the wheel hard over and braked violently, broadsiding the Bentley round the curve in a shower of dust and small stones. Once round, with the nose pointing in the right direction, he kept the throttle pedal flat on the floor. For a moment the rear wheels scrabbled at the gravel surface, then the deep-treaded tyres bit into the road and the car streaked up the rise just as the nose of the tractor poked out of the gateway. Steed got past as the blue and yellow Ferguson was starting a wide turn to the far side of the road so that the trailer with its tall load would not foul the gatepost. The Mercedes would be coming round the corner, he calculated, when the narrow roadway was just about blocked.

As he scraped through the narrowing gap he had a momentary impression of the tractor driver's face, mouth dropped open in surprise to see the great green sports car racing past. On top of the load. two bronzed labourers in overalls sat perspiring in the straw. Then he was past and away to the next corner. As he lifted his foot for an instant to make the change up into third, he heard from behind the wild scroop of urgently applied brakes, the squeal of locked wheels.

He drove round the corner, turned right at a T-junction and bumped over a level crossing. The road stretched ahead for two hundred yards and then disappeared around the corner of an inn. Just before taking the bend, he looked back over his shoulder.

The Mercedes was on the level crossing. Its offside front wing was crumpled and there were clods of earth and bits of grass between the bumper and the shattered headlamp. But it was coming up fast.

Steed sighed with exasperation. The driver of the black saloon was good. He must have clapped all the anchors on and then, as the obstruction moved slowly across the road, squeezed past behind the tail of the trailer, taking a piece of bank with him as he went . . .

The undercover man put everything he knew into his driving. He was safe only as long as he could keep to the narrow, twisting lanes where the Bentley's superior cornering could place it at a decisive advantage. As long as the flat, green back of the British car was disappearing round one bend as the black snout of the Merc appeared round the one before, he was able to prevent the sharpshooters from taking proper aim. But as soon as there was a straight bit of road, and the Mercedes gained on him, he was at an enormous tactical disadvantage.

He tried to tempt the driver to overcook it on the corners — and above the thunder of the Bentley's progress round the tight, sharp bends, the continuous squealing of tyres from behind testified to the pursuer's difficulties on a curve with the big, softly-sprung saloon.

But despite the noise, he did get the car round. He wouldn't be tempted. If necessary, he simply slowed down and waited for a straight patch on which to catch up again.

Steed was beginning to wonder if he would ever get rid of them. He could of course have driven to a town centre, stopped the car and got out — and been perfectly safe. They could hardly have shot him down in a crowded street and got away with it. But he had to get to London — and therefore he had to stay with the car.

There was also the question of petrol. Once or twice in the last few miles, they had taken snap shots at him on short straights, and he had felt several jars as the bullets had plunked into the Bentley somewhere behind. Despite the forty-gallon capacity of the tank, and even if it was not holed, the consumption was very heavy. Sometime or other, he would have to stop. He was wondering how best he could put this fact to his advantage when the road ran out from under the shade of a plantation of fir trees — and the topography altered before his eyes. Instead of tumbling about in short, steep valleys and wooded hillocks, the countryside now spread away in a wide undulation broken only here and there by the serrations of hedge and tree. The fields, instead of being small and enclosed, stretched wide and open with verges of downland grasses bending before a slight breeze.

At the horizon of this upland plain a long line of people stretched two or three deep across the skyline. Nearer, a number of cars were parked beside the road and one field, boasting a notice saying *Park 2s 6d*, was filled with neat rows of vehicles nose to tail.

The road swung nearer the file of people. Beyond them as he raced across the flat stretch, he could see the roofs of wooden buildings and what looked like a railway station footbridge showing above a swell of land to the west. There were other cars, too, going in the same direction that he was, and at about the same speed. He could see the heads and shoulders of the drivers over the crowd. Farther across, a structure like a guard tower in a prisoner-of-war compound reared into the sky.

He had arrived on one of the perimeter roads circling Silverstone race track. With the Mercedes in hot pursuit, he drove rapidly down behind the row of spectators. A voice, monstrous and distorted blared inhumanly from four zinc speakers grouped at the top of a pole.

There must be a club meeting in progress, Steed thought. There weren't enough cars or people about for it to be an international meeting—or officious busybodies either, he told himself with a grin. Had it been, he would certainly have been peremptorily waved down by angry officials before now! A little farther on, a sign-board confirmed his guess. *Vintage Sports-Car Club—Silverstone Meeting*, he read. *No Admittance to Circuit. For Grandstand, Pits and Paddock: 2nd on Left*. And there was a finger pointing back in the direction from which he had come.

Silverstone was once an airfield, and just beyond the notice a section of runway linked the perimeter road with the circuit before continuing across the fields in the centre of the course and disappearing over the brow of the hill. Two pairs of oil drums, each connected by a striped red and white pole, barred the way between road and track. A small group of young men with tweed caps and brassards stood by a line of straw bales just beyond.

But there was nothing coupling one linked pair of drums with the other.

An impish grin twisted Steed's lips. He braked, turned right and drove through between the two pairs of drums at full tilt, crossing the circuit and continuing up the broad runway towards the centre of the track.

The competing cars were all out of sight somewhere round on the far side of the course, so the Mercedes was able to follow him practically without slackening speed. Steed looked back as he accelerated up the runway to hear the squeal of its wide-based tyres and see the stunned consternation with which the tweed-capped young men greeted this double infringement of their authority . . .

The decomposed concrete surface of the old runway was extremely rough, yet the great width of it, added to the wide, open character of the country itself, contributed to minimise the impression of speed, and the undercover man saw to his surprise on glancing at the tachometer that he was doing nearly ninety miles per hour again. The black saloon was once more gaining on him, its modern, independent springing making lighter work of the bumps than Steed's stiffly sprung sports car. But soon they were over the brow of the rise and belting down towards the long, low lines of the pits, grandstands and the paddock.

The field shot past the end of the runway just before Steed reached it. He recognised two Bugattis—a Type 27 GP and a Brescia—a much-modified 8-litre Bentley with an enormous bonnet and hardly any body, several fish-shaped vehicles including an Amilcar, a GP Salmson and what he thought might be an early Aston Martin, and the spidery shapes of a number of chain-driven Frazer-Nashes.

The runway joined the track at an acute angle—a corner deceptively sharp insofar as its width disguised the fact that it should be treated almost as a hairpin. Seeing no better alternative, Steed decided to join the race until he could find an opportunity to leave the circuit: it was safer for the competitors than if he circulated in a contrary direction. There was no way out directly opposite.

He changed down into third, braked, took a line through the curve, and discovered too late that he had been misled by the acuteness of the turn.

The Bentley was going too fast. Understeering, it moved farther and farther over to the left-hand side of the track as the

corner unwound more and more sharply to the right. Eventually
Steed ran out of road, over-corrected, slewed sideways across
the track as he lost the back end momentarily, tweaked the
wheel to bring the car back to heel—and put his foot down to
regain full adhesion. As he straightened up to follow the other
cars, he found himself alongside an impeccably turned out
supercharged 1750 Alfa Romeo with long, tapered mudguards
and an exquisite body by Zagato. The driver—a wizened little
man fully sixty years old—turned and grinned at Steed and
gave the thumbs-up sign.

The Mercedes hadn't been so lucky. Its driver had misjudged
the turn completely. The inverse camber rear wheels, with their
built-in oversteer, began directing the front of the car as he
slammed into the corner far too fast, nosing it into the right
hand side more and more until the back end broke away completely and the big car spun slowly round three times before
coming to rest with its tail among the straw bales.

Steed profited by the delay as the driver re-started and drove
back on to the track by threading his way up through the
competitors in the race.

The sun was low down in the sky now, stroking long shadows
across the grass from a row of trees behind the grandstand.
It winked and glittered on the coachwork of the massed cars
ranged in the car parks, glared from the huge glass windows of
the timekeeper's hut, and caused the sprinkling of people in the
stands to shade their eyes. Across the width of the track a dense
crowd watched the racing from the concrete parapet above the
extended line of pits counters. Behind them in the paddock, an
ambulant throng watched competitors tuning, testing, reassem-
bling or merely tinkering with a great variety of vintage
machinery.

After the cars had snarled past the pits and disappeared under
the footbridge, the voice of the commentator could once again
be heard over the P.A. system.

"... this second lap of the final Five-Lap Handicap of this
afternoon's programme, it was MacDollar in the Anzani Frazer-
Nash leading Arnelo-Fenster in the 8-litre Bentley and Hodge
in the Bugatti—I say! ... By Jove, a most frightfully queer
thing's happened! There were nine starters in this race—and
now—and now ... why, there seem to be eleven cars on the
track! ... I say, I don't know if you can confirm that over at

*Abbey Curve, can you? Can you let me know, old boy, how
many clients you have at Abbey?"*

And then the other voice, high-pitched, excited: *"Yes, Good
Lord, you're absolutely right. There seems to be a blower four-
and-a-half extra to the old tally . . . and a—yes, and a piece of
modern tinware! Teutonic tinware at that. A Merc 220—"*

*"The 300 actually, old boy, I think you'll find. The bigger
body."*

*"Yes . . . yes, the 300. Thank you, Bill: you're absolutely
right. Yes, a Merc 300—the fuel-injection model, I believe—
and it seems to be full of chaps. The Bentley's carving its way
up through the field . . . lying about fourth now, I should say
. . . passing Lindale's Ulster Austin on the inside and— Oh, now,
I say, really! That's a bit naughty! Oo, that WAS naughty. The
Merc's shoved Bagley-Worsthamstow's Aston-Martin off the
track coming into the straight. NOT the action of a post-vintage
thoroughbred at all!"*

At the far side of the course, John Steed was enjoying a minor
dice with the driver of the Alfa Romeo as they passed a bunch
of the slower cars coming out of a bend. Then, all at once,
there was a thunderous roar on his offside and the 8-litre Bentley
drew level, having obviously lapped the entire field. The driver
pushed his visor up over the peak of his crash helmet and
leaned over his empty passenger seat to call across to the undercover man. "What the devil do you think you're doing?" he
shouted, his moustache bristling with rage. "Don't you know
the four-and-a-halfs have all been kept back until the last race
to compete with 30/98s? I'll have you black-flagged for this!
. . . and the BDC will hear of it." He snapped down his visor
and turned to his front again, his vast machine slowly forging
ahead of Steed's.

But behind, Steed saw over his shoulder, the Mercedes was
as relentlessly approaching, having recovered from its spin three-
quarters of a lap before and made up the lost ground.

Characteristically, he made up his mind on the instant. The
circuit veered away to the right here, but on the outside of the
bend the remains of another runway led to a minor road. There
were no marshals on the outside of the corner and the crowd
was very sparse. Steed waved goodbye to the astonished driver
of the Alfa and pulled across to the left hand side of the track.
He took the curve into the runway on two wheels with the black

Mercedes close behind. Straw bales went spinning as the two cars snarled up the wide concrete path towards the entrance to the lane three hundred yards away.

Steed changed into top at about 60. Not far before the gate, two Nissen huts stood side by side in the middle of the boundary fence defining the limits of the course. The wire-and-post barrier was joined on to the outsides of the two buildings—but between them a narrow concreted space led through without hindrance to a flat field.

When he was nearly level with the first hut, Steed stamped on the brake pedal, knocked the gear lever into neutral, blipped twice decisively on the accelerator pedal, and slid the lever straight across the gate and into second. The needle on the rev. counter tore round the face of the instrument as he swung the car in a very wide circle towards the huts and headed for the gap between them.

One of the things about the older Bentleys is that, from the driving seat, you can see at all times the tops of all four wings —which means that your judging of distances in relation to the car can be superb.

Because of the wide sweep it had taken, Steed's car now approached the narrow gap between the huts head on. The network of fine lines around his eyes tightened and a muscle flickered along his jaw as he steered, without a moment's hesitation, flat out for the opening. The Bentley surged forward and leaped for the gap.

It howled through at about forty-five miles per hour. There were perhaps two-and-a-half to three inches to spare on either side.

This time the Mercedes did fall into the trap. They had been taking long shots at Steed all the way up the runway and, just before he had turned, a third hole pierced his windscreen and a long splinter of wood had furrowed itself up from the dashboard. Now, scenting success at last, the driver took the opportunity of closing up even more by cutting the corner which Steed had taken so wide.

Which meant that he approached the opening between the huts at a slant instead of straight ahead.

The nose of the wide car angled in to the gap—and then, too late, the driver saw his mistake. But at 50 miles per hour one has no time to make corrections for an initial error like that.

As he braked fiercely and hauled on the wheel to pull the car away from the wall of the far hut, the nearside of the saloon slammed into the corner of the nearer hut.

The Mercedes shuddered and leaped. Its rear end arc-ed into the air to fall with a crash against the wall of the far hut. There was a scream of distorted steel and a shattering of glass. For a moment the crescendo of an engine freed from all load screeched into the air. Then the dull bloomp of an explosion obliterated all else in an inferno of flame.

On the far side of the passageway, the Bentley was bouncing to a halt on the rough, tussocky ground of the field. Steed looked back at the dense column of flame-tinged smoke that was already billowing into the air between the huts. He shrugged his shoulders and steered the car, bumping, across the field and down a shallow bank into the lane.

Five minutes later, the wind was blowing a chord through the three bullet holes in his windscreen—and Steed was whistling an improvisation on it—as the Bentley sped down the main road to Buckingham and London.

15

THE NIGHT THE VANS LEFT EARLY

Posters advertising the Sunday papers were still leaning against the walls of Fleet Street as Steed arrived. *British Ambassador's Car Overturned*, one announced; *Sir George Carew—The Truth!* promised another. *Anti-British Riots in Rotterdam; Troops Called In*, a third declared. Steed raised an eyebrow and drove on to the *Courier*. They'd have more sensational news still, if he wasn't able to unmask The Brotherhood that night . . .

He parked the Bentley outside the Court in Greening's Row. The damage wasn't as bad as he'd feared: the car had been hit eleven times in all—three times through the windscreen, once each on dashboard, tonneau cover and rear-view mirror, and five times in the back. One of these *had* holed the petrol tank— but above the thirty-gallon level, so that no fuel had in fact been lost. The other four had penetrated the curved corner of the body to one side of the spare wheel and lodged in the squab of the back seat.

He dismissed the chase from his mind and hurried into the *Courier* building. Somebody there was operating the keyboard of a teleprinter sending the special instructions to Hanningford.

The rest of the fake outside fold of the paper was compiled from instructions teleprinted in the routine way to Manchester —obtained via a leak machine in the *Clarion*'s offices. But somebody here was cutting out the Manchester line when the top story instructions were sent, and substituting the forged speech reports. At all costs, he must locate that machine and identify its operator.

Fortunately, one fact narrowed the field considerably. Whoever was doing it had to know what the real front page was like —otherwise they would not know what size, shape or length to make the bogus story, so that it fitted perfectly.

In practice, this meant the machine he was looking for would have to be somewhere near one of the editorial floors.

The top eight floors housed accounts departments, syndication divisions, the personnel branch and other administrative offices, apart from Borridale's personal suite. Together with the advertising department on the third floor, they would have been locked up at five thirty on a weekday and would not have been in use at all on a Sunday. He could safely ignore them, therefore.

There were no teleprinters at all on the seventh, sixth or fifth floors, which housed the photographic department, the photo library and the process department respectively. And the fourth housed only one from each of the newsagencies, so that subs working on the stone could keep an eye on the latest developments.

The most likely place to find the machine he was looking for was thus among the managerial offices on the eighth floor, in the library on the first, or on the main editorial floor. He decided to explore this, the most difficult, first, and ran up the stairs leading to the second floor.

Here, at one side of the newsroom, with a constant service of messengers to the subs' table, was the teleprinter room itself. Receivers from all the agencies—Reuters, Associated Press, United Press, Exchange Telegraph and the Press Association—vied with the *Courier*'s own direct lines from Paris, New York and Manchester in the continual clatter. A further bank of machines supplied information to the library, and most of the managerial offices on the eighth had one or other of the services. Steed's self-imposed task was to identify which, of the machines that could also be used for transmitting, was in contact with Hanningford.

In the bustle which surrounds the production of a mass-circulation daily newspaper, it is fairly easy for one member of the staff who has no particular job on hand to move about unnoticed—providing he looks as if he knows where he is going and has the right answer ready if challenged. Steed always looked as if he knew where he was going and had never been caught without the right answer ready. Unobtrusively, swiftly, accurately, he set about eliminating the unlikely machines and finding the one he wanted.

It was over an hour before he succeeded in locating it. He sauntered casually past a row of machines in an empty office on the eighth floor, glancing casually at the paper being ejected

from the four teleprinters behind the door. Three of them were
agency machines. The fourth was a leak from the Manchester
line. It was busy with last minute alterations to the centre-
spread. As he watched, the take ended and the operator signed
off with a "back in ten minutes" tag. The machine whirred and
then relapsed into silence.

He poked his head into the office next door. It, too, was
unoccupied—but only temporarily. A cigarette lay across an
ashtray, its glowing end spiralling smoke into the air. Beside it,
steam rose from the surface of a half-finished mug of coffee.

There were three transmitter-receiver machines—squat,
modern shapes on a specially-built bench—which were linked
with the *Courier's* own lines to Manchester, Paris and New
York, and two agency teleprinters of the normal console type
reaching to the floor. The agency machines were working and so
was one of the *Courier's*. He looked across to see which it was.

It was the teleprinter on the direct line to Manchester—the
line from which the operator had signed off for ten minutes
only a moment before . . .

In two strides Steed crossed the room. The machine was
transmitting. The electronic head was ingesting a long curl of
pre-punched tape which had been prepared and left on a spool,
and was now feeding itself through automatically.

Steed looked above the keyboard to read the duplicate of
what the tape was sending.

Underneath the sign-off take that he had seen in the adjoining
office, the lines were spelling themselves out:

1953 LDN 2 SPL FOR HANNINGFD 0908 FOR 1008 TAKE
TWENTYTHREE

IN LAST PAR OF LEAD DELETE FINAL SENTENCE AND SUBSTITUTE
FOLLOWING BEGINS COLON QUOTE THIS COUNTRY WILL IMPOSE
SEVERE ECONOMIC SANCTIONS ON ANXXX ANY EUROPEAN
GOVERNMENT NOT RECOGNISING BRITAINS LEQXXXX LEQXXXX
LEADERSHIP UNQUOTE THE PREMIER SAID. REQUOTE IT IS TIME
WE STOPPED PANDERING TO BLACKMAILING . . .

Steed looked up quickly. Footsteps were tapping along the
corridor outside. In a single lithe move he was behind the door,
flattened against the wall.

The footsteps turned in at the office door. Steed held his

breath.

The door was opened and pushed back so that it partially hid the room from his view. Whoever it was walked across the office and through a door on the far side into an inner room. The door of the inner room closed.

Steed slipped out into the corridor and ran for the lifts.

In Fetter Lane he found an untenanted telephone call box and dialled a very secret number in three groups of three. It rang once and the line was opened. Nobody announced the number or said anything.

In a low voice, the undercover man asked for another number, even more secret, a number known to less than thirty people in the country. He heard the burr-burr of the automatic ringing tone three times, followed by a click and a man's voice saying: "Control."

"Steed."

"Identification?"

"First wicket down; slow leg breaks; cover point."

"Go ahead, Steed."

"I need urgent information. Can you get R.S.2 to find something out from Somerset House on a Sunday night?"

"Of course."

"Good. I'm speaking on an open line. From a call box. You know where I am—I can't take the risk of calling from there."

"Understood."

"I want to know if a certain party ever changed their name by deed poll—and if they did, what the former name was. If it was changed, it would have been between 1945 and 1948, I should think."

"Right."

"You'll have to call me back—you know where. I'll leave word with the switchboard which extension. And when you phone, watch it. I don't know how safe or dangerous the lines are. Just give me the name—if there has been a change— nothing else. If not, say nothing doing."

"Yes. What's the present name of the party?"

Steed told him.

"Very well," the voice said. "It'll take a half hour or so."

"I'll be waiting," Steed said, and rang off.

He was sitting at a table in the *Courier*'s library exactly twenty-seven minutes later when the bespectacled, middle-aged spinster who was duty librarian called over to him: "Are you Mr Steed of the Warr column? . . . You are? Oh, then there's a call for you on my phone. Over here."

Steed thanked her and picked up the receiver. The voice was as curt as ever. "Steed?"

"Yes."

"Crandell Robins. Nineteen forty-six."

"Thank you very much. Splendid. You're two and a quarter minutes early, though."

"We don't appreciate levity in this department, Steed. Your watch is thirty seconds slow."

The agent smiled, put down the instrument and went through to the "personalities" section of the library. He walked past the rows of identical grey filing cabinets to the political division and scanned the deep drawers with their identifying cards. When he came to the drawer marked *Rinaldi—Ross,* he stopped and pulled it out to its full extent. Rapidly he flicked over the tops of the close-packed folders within.

There was a file for *ROBINS, Crandell.* In it were a dozen or more of the pieces of paper which the *Courier* librarians used for pasting up cuttings. Each sheet was headed with a typed legend giving the name of the newspaper from which the cutting had been taken, and the date on which it had appeared. At the foot of the leaves, details of what page the story had been on, and in what position, had been added in ink.

But of the cuttings themselves, there was no sign. Every one had been removed.

Steed went back to the General section. Ten minutes research brought him to another drawer in which, after ferreting about for a little while, he discovered a second file on Mr Crandell Robins. There were fewer entries in this folder—but in each case they, too, had had the cuttings ripped out.

Whoever it was that was covering up for this man couldn't possibly have plundered every file in Fleet Street, however. Steed hurried out and ran down to the Reuter building at No. 85. He had friends in the Press Association on the second floor —and in a few minutes he was once again seated before a library table. The P.A. did have a file on Crandell Robins, a much thicker folder than either of those at the *Courier*—thirty or forty sheets at least. And in this case, every leaf had a cutting on it.

It was an old scandal now, the backing sheets dusty and yellow. The last entry was a *London Gazette* announcement in September, 1946.

But it seemed to absorb Steed. He pored over the cuttings for some time, making occasional notes on a piece of the copy paper provided at the table.

The first entry was a photograph. Published in a *Globe* of 1937, it showed Robins—the features distinctive even then—among a group of volunteers returning from the civil war in Spain. They had been fighting with the Franco forces against the government.

The next few sheets were cuttings of police court proceedings. Robins had been charged with insulting behaviour, with breaches of the peace, with common assault—all of the charges arising from Jew-baiting demonstrations in the East End with the fascists. On most of the charges he had been fined, but a grievous bodily harm charge had been dropped—and in a civil case for damages brought against him by a Jewish shopkeeper whose premises had been vandalised, the jury found against the plaintiff. Several cuttings quoted him speaking in support of Mosley at public meetings. In 1939 he had made an impassioned plea for an alliance with Hitler and had publicly repudiated his membership of the British Union of Fascists because they were not sufficiently militant. A newspaper interview soon after quoted him as saying that he proposed to start his own right-wing party on a "Britain for the British" platform.

He had been photographed shaking hands with Goering and Himmler. He had been narrowly defeated in a Midlands by-election. He had been pelted with fruit and vegetables in August, 1939, when he tried to address an open-air meeting at Trafalgar Square. And during the war he had been detained on the Isle of Man under Regulation 18b.

Before the *London Gazette* cutting announcing his change of name, there were only two further entries after that. One reported—as a gossip column item—that he had been sacked from a job as a feature writer in a Sunday newspaper after the National Union of Journalists chapel had discovered his past history and made representations to the management. The other was a report of a manifesto that he had circularised to the press in 1946.

It had announced the formation of a new political party of

the right wing, the name and intentions of which would be promulgated later "to those of our supporters whom we know we can trust and on whose unstinted aid we know we can rely".

Steed whistled to himself as he closed the file and got to his feet. "So they've been planning this for twenty years!" he said aloud. "All working away in the darkness there, scrabbling about under the surface while we thought it had been long forgotten . . ."

He went back to the *Courier* and walked quietly along the corridor to the office where he had discovered the teleprinter sending instructions to Hanningford. There wasn't a sound from inside. The door was ajar.

He peered through the crack. None of the printers was working and the place seemed deserted. Through the uncurtained windows, lights from buildings across the street gleamed through the late August dusk. Steed slipped through the door and shone his flashlight at the bank of teleprinters. Their silence was immediately explained: they had all been switched off and the master plug pulled out. He directed the beam at the Manchester machine. After a great wedge of material rounding off the genuine instructions to the north, a final message to Hanningford lay just above the perspex level.

2017 LON 2 SPL FOR H'FORD. TAKE THIRTYTWO. OK G'BYE FOR NOW SIGNING OFF ALL COMPLETE. SEE U LATER + + + + +

He heard the swish of nylon stockings and half turned his head. But he didn't hear the swish of the sock half filled with sand which described a short arc in the air and thumped into his hair just above the ear. He dropped to the ground like a stone and all the lights went out.

Sandra Gillan smiled scornfully as she came out from her hiding place behind the door. She pulled her white silk shirt down taut over her remarkable breasts and tucked it further into the waist-band of her leather skirt. Then, inserting the toe of one black boot under Steed's inert body and turning him over on to his back so that she could move the door freely, she looked swiftly once around the office, locked up, and walked rapidly down the passage towards the lifts.

*   *   *

Steed rolled over and woke with a groan. The room was completely dark and there was an inferno of pain in his head. Agonisingly, he raised himself to his knees. He shook his head in an attempt to clear his brain. Gradually, in the diffuse light seeping through the windows from the lamps below, the room assembled itself shape by shadowy shape before his eyes. Somewhere out in the night an intermittent neon sign pulsed regular injections of pink light at the sky.

Steed's groping hands touched the edge of a desk. He hauled himself up and collapsed into a chair. There was a carafe and glass on the desk. He poured himself water and drank greedily. After a few minutes the clamour in his head died down a little and he could begin to think again.

The time, the time—what was the time?

In anguish, he looked at the luminous dial of his watch. It was almost nine o'clock. The genuine continental editions would have been printed some time ago. In another quarter of an hour they would be leaving by van for the north—where the fake front pages for which he had seen the teleprinted instructions would be substituted for the real ones.

Whatever happened, he had to stop them getting there.

He lurched to his feet and went to the door. It was locked. Fortunately he was carrying the miniature metal toolbox shaped like a cigarette case. He switched on the light and set to work on the lock. Four minutes later he was shambling down the corridor, reeling against the walls as he tried desperately to clear his head. At the lift shaft, he pressed the button for the left-hand car (there were several scars on the metal as a result of their little excursion the day before, he noticed) and rose to the sixteenth floor.

By the grace of God the lord was back—playing Tchaikovsky's *Nutcracker Suite* on his hi-fi. He took one look at Steed and led him to an armchair. "Brandy. A large glass. That's what you need," he barked. "Not a word, my dear fellow—not a word until it's all gone."

Steed swallowed the smooth, mellow spirit and felt better at once. "I'm sorry to crash in on you," he said at last. "But you've got to do something. You're the only one who can—and it's got to be done very quickly. You'll have to take my word for it that it's necessary."

"Tell me about it," Borridale said crisply.

Briefly, Steed sketched in the events which had led up to his ambush in the office below.

"All right," the press lord said when he had finished. "I'll take your word for it, Steed. You are sure?"

"Absolutely, I'm afraid."

"Right. I'll call the despatch right away." He moved over to his desk, picked up the house phone and dialled a number.

"Hallo? Borridale here . . . Is Mr Mailer there? . . . Bring him to the telephone please. It's urgent . . . Mailer? Borridale. Look —the five-stars about to leave on the van for Leicester East: hold up the shipment at all costs. It's going to—*What*! What did you say? . . . They did? . . . Oh, it was, was it? . . . Did he? I see. Yes—yes, thank you very much . . . No. Not now, I guess." He put the instrument down and turned to Steed. "The vans left a half hour early tonight," he said hoarsely. "Special instructions from Mr Creighton."

"There's still a chance," Steed said. "May I use your phone?"

"Be my guest."

The undercover man picked up the extension instrument and asked the switchboard to get him the Queen's Hotel at Hanningford.

"I feel rather guilty about Mrs Peel anyway," he said to Borridale as he waited. "I promised to call her every hour and —er—various things supervened." He rubbed the swelling above his ear ruefully. "Hallo? Hallo, is that the Queen's Hotel, Hanningford?"

"Queen's Hotel here," the voice of the friendly night porter said. "Whom do you want please?"

"This is John Steed here. I should like—"

"Mr Steed! How are you? You're all right then?"

"Very well thank you. I'd like—What d'you mean, I'm all right, then?"

"From the accident, Mr Steed. We was worried about you."

"Accident?" Steed asked, a sudden sinking feeling manifesting itself in the pit of his stomach.

"Why, yes. Wasn't you in a smash on the M.1? Two traffic cops come on their bicycles with a patrol car not long after you left and asked for Mrs Peel. Told her you'd been badly knocked about in a smash with a lorry and were asking for her at the hospital. Taken you to Northampton, they had—or so the man said."

"And Mrs Peel?"

"Why, I thought she'd be with you! She went off in the patrol car with the cops . . ."

16

DILEMMA FOR EMMA

THE oldest trick in the whole wide world, Emma Peel thought bitterly to herself—and she'd fallen for it, hook, line and sinker, as they used to say. She hadn't even been suspicious when she had noticed that there were no handles on the insides of the doors of the "police car". To stop crooks escaping after they had been arrested, she had thought!

She had first become alarmed when she had seen the uniformed man in the passenger seat begin to wind up the glass partition between the front and back of the car. "What are you doing?" she had cried sharply.

"Keep you out of the draught, lady," the man replied. But he had a smirk on his face as he said it. The thick plate glass slid home into a groove in the roof. Emma, looking around in something of a panic, had seen the speaking tube and snatched it up. "Where are we going," she had begun imperiously. "If you think you can get away with—" But too late she had recognised the faint, cloying, rubbery smell drifting from the mouthpiece of the tube. It was trilene, the "twilight sleep" anaesthetic—and the gas was being pumped into the back of the car via the speaking tube.

She had tried desperately to reach a window, to break the glass, to wave even and attract somebody's attention. But the street and the houses and the people had seemed suddenly terribly far away and small—and the window was far away, too (surely it was getting farther away still?). Lifting an arm was even more difficult than . . . than . . . what was it called? And why was the floor getting so *soft* . . . In an instant of abrupt clarity, she had been aware of the grooved, gritty feel of the car's rubber floor mat against her cheek. And then the darkness washed over her in steady waves . . .

Now she was awake in a place full of machinery, a place she had been in before, hadn't she? But of course, yes— the *Clarion* works at . . . what was the name of the place? Hanningford. Yes, that was it: Hanningford. And all she could think of was how glad she was it had been trilene, because trilene had no after effects and all the other anaesthetics made her violently sick. And really she felt tremendously well; she felt marvellous . . . except—oh, yes. She was lying flat on her back, bound to some kind of steel table.

The table, large and rectangular, seemed to be part of some machine. Emma's legs were separated and tied to two of the corners; her arms, stretched wide above her head, to the other two. She was wearing the black jersey catsuit she had worn when she and Steed burgled the *Courier* building the night before—and thus spreadeagled, the dark and supple outlines of her body reflected dully from the polished surface of a second steel slab which was canted at an angle over the table at a height of about eighteen inches from her head. Beyond her feet, so far as she could see—her limbs were stretched almost to dislocation point—was a dirty white wall along which were ranged cabinets full of shallow drawers. There was an iron wheel just behind her head. And somewhere in the distance a light machine clanked metallically.

Somebody advanced and stood beside the machine to which she was tied and stood looking down at her—a bulky woman in a tightly belted black mackintosh. Something about the way she stood, something about the manner in which her heavy figure creased the stiff, shiny material stirred a chord in Emma's mind.

"You're the woman who tried to kill me in Amsterdam," she said, looking up with a flash of intuition.

The woman nodded her straw coloured head. "That's right, dear," she said, the familiarity sounding almost obscene on her lips. "And I shall probably try again later tonight—only this time I shall succeed. But first we have a little quiz game to play, you and I." Her voice was hoarse, a little heavy to match her body, with a trace of accent that Emma could not quite place.

She unbelted her raincoat and started to undo the buttons, nodding to somebody behind Emma's head. The girl swivelled her eyes upwards. Into her field of vision a man's hand came and grasped a wooden handle projecting from the rim of the iron wheel. He twirled the wheel. As the arc of it that Emma could see spun greasily round, the steel plate to which she was bound moved bodily sideways, towards the woman. At the end of its travel there was a slight jolt: obviously it ran on some kind of rails.

The woman took off her mackintosh—beneath it she was shapeless in a blue denim boiler suit—and dropped it deliberately across Emma's legs. The girl felt the cold weight of it on her thighs.

"You're lying on the platen of a press," the woman said roughly. "When George there spins that wheel again, it slides back under the inclined plate—and the plate can be brought down so that it's horizontal, parallel to the one you're on. It's exactly the same size as yours, dear, and it's half an inch thick —very heavy. Now on top of the plate is a big, threaded screw with a handle each side so that two people can turn it. And when you turn it, it screws the plate down towards the platen you're lying on."

The woman regarded Emma in silence for a moment. Then she went on, her voice suddenly silky with anticipation: "And do you know, dear, if that screw is turned far enough, it brings the plate right down on to the platen, quite flat; so tight you couldn't get a sheet of paper between them . . . I wonder what would happen if we did that when you were lying *on* the platen?"

Emma stared expressionlessly up into her eyes.

"It would hurt dreadfully, I'm sure," the woman said. "But that's what George and I are going to do, just to see what happens, if you aren't a good girl and don't answer our questions —George! Don't be bashful: come out and be introduced."

A rat-faced little man with a ragged moustache edged shiftily round in front of Emma. He licked his lips, eyeing her taut figure with a wolfish smile.

"Evening. She's a caution, Hilde is," he said conversationally, nodding towards the woman. "A real caution."

"Right," the woman called Hilde said with an abrupt change of tone. "Here are the first four questions: What were you doing here this afternoon? Who is Steed? Who are you both working for? And why have they sent you prying and nosing about in other people's business?"

"I don't know what you are talking about," Emma said.

Hilde leaned down and slapped her hard, twice, across the face. The blows were delivered separately, at a considered interval, with a substantial backswing—and they hurt. One of them caught her partially on the nose, and to Emma's fury tears spurted uncontrollably from her eyes. "I'm asking you again. And I want an answer," Hilde was saying.

"I tell you I've no idea what you mean."

"Very well," the woman said. "I can't say I'm sorry, for I'm always interested in an experiment. We'll put a bit of pressure on you to see if we can *make* you answer." And she laughed wheezily at her joke, gesturing to George to return to the wheel.

"Oh, she's a knock-out, she is," George said to Emma. "She takes our Indoctrination and Information lectures. You ought to see her Practicals—they're a riot!" He spun the wheel and Emma and her steel table slid smoothly back under the inclined metal plate. Together, George and Hilde lowered the top plate until it was horizontal. Then they mounted a steel step on the far side of the machine and worked at the giant screw. The metal plate hid them from Emma's view, but she could hear the steel screeching faintly as the thread bit into its grooves.

Slowly, inexorably, the half-inch thick steel plate descended until it was just touching the tips of her breasts. She could feel the dead, cold pressure of it through her clothes.

The woman Hilde was shouting some question above the rattle of the machine at the far end of the shop. George appeared at Emma's side and felt about with one hand between the two steel slabs. "Yes—just touching," he called back.

With the cold metal almost at her cheekbone, Emma lay with her head to one side and heard the voice of Hilde behind her. "I'm going to ask you one more time, dear. And if you don't answer, we will go back to the screw. But please understand this—when we go back we shall screw for two minutes. And we will continue for two minutes, even if you change your mind and decide to talk before then—at my age I cannot keep going up and down this stair all day."

There was a neighing laugh from George, and then Hilde again: "Now—think well before you refuse, dear. Who is John Steed?"

Fighting down a rising panic of claustrophobia, Emma replied in a strangled voice: "I've never heard of him."

Footsteps retreated, then clanged on the iron stair. The clatter of the machine continued. The scrooping of the press began again.

Emma was first conscious of it as a sensation of difficulty in breathing. She was unable to expand her lungs as much as she wished—and that meant that the quicker, shallower breathing she was forced to adopt itself sounded in her ears like an increase in the panic she felt. The first pain came when the steel plate touched the toes of her boots and forced her feet outwards. Immovably spreadeagled as she was, there was no movement she could make to alleviate it. Then came the insufferable, relentless weight on the rib-cage. How long had passed? A half minute? A quarter? A minute? She bit back a groan and wondered whether her reason or her body would collapse first.

And then suddenly she was aware that the pressure had not increased for some time. The noise of the machine had stopped and a phone was ringing somewhere.

It must have been quite near to her, for she could hear clearly the voice of Hilde: "Okay, darling . . . I see . . . Yes, yes, I will . . . Yes, we can see to all that, don't worry. Now what about the girl? . . . Very well, we'll do that—but you're spoiling my fun! . . . See you soon, darling."

The ginny voice was raised. "Listen everybody, please. That was Sandra. There's been a change of plan. The shipment's coming a half hour earlier than usual. Now, it's terribly urgent —our front pages have to be substituted even more quickly. And the planes must be ready for instant take-off. Milton, go and phone the airfield, will you? . . . All right, please—let's go. And we do everything *twice* as fast as normal—for the party!"

Emma found the pause almost worse than the torture. Then abruptly light flooded in on her as heavy iron chucks were slid to one side and the top slab was lifted back to its inclined position. She breathed deeply, deeply in the sheer joy of being able to.

"I am sorry to have to postpone our little experiment, dear," Hilde was saying, "but our plans have changed and I am ordered to take you off here and prepare you for a little journey with us. Now we have to tie you a different way—but first, please be careful." She produced a small automatic and pointed it at Emma as George laboriously untied first her legs and then her hands.

"Stand up now," Hilde said, "and put your hands behind you."

Emma stood up. But the big woman had made the cardinal

error of underestimating an opponent—and allowing her too
close to the gun. In a single fluid movement, Emma threw herself backwards onto the platen and kicked the automatic spinning high into the air from Hilde's hand, as she slid across the
smooth steel and cannoned into George.

The little man was slightly built but he was wiry, and he had
been taught something about unarmed combat. He side-stepped
neatly as Emma hurtled at him off the platen and chopped her
down to the floor with a rabbit punch. As she rolled over, he
dived at her with hands outstretched—but Emma doubled up
her legs under her chin, straightening them with a jerk as he was
about to land. The soles of her feet caught him in the solar
plexus and lifted him up and over her head. He crashed to the
ground somewhere behind her.

Emma scrambled to her feet. Hilde was on her hands and
knees groping underneath one of cabinets for the gun. Half
a dozen men in overalls, interrupted in their work by the noise,
were running up from the far end of the machine room. Behind
her, there was only George—rising somewhat groggily to
his feet with the support of a four-wheeled loading trolley.

The girl spun round. Hilde's mackintosh was lying on the
ground where it had fallen when she rose from the platen.
She snatched it up and flung it over George's head, pushing
him backwards on to the trolley—then, seizing the rail with
both hands, she swung the trolley round on its castored wheels
and sent it careering down the aisle between the presses towards
the men approaching her. Trapped between bulks of machinery,
they were unable to get out of the way of the speeding car.
With George's struggling, semi-enveloped body on board, it
smashed into them and knocked them down in a heap.

Emma was dashing for the heavy door leading to the entrance
hall and the stairs. She hauled it open and slipped through.

The main doors leading to the street were guarded by a short
barrel-chested man with a heavy chin. He was carrying a
rubber truncheon and wearing a black brassard on his arm
with a gold B on it. The girl halted, turned left, and fled up
the stairs as the man started towards her.

From the first floor landing, she could see through into the
offices where more men in brassards were clearing up layout
sheets, piles of copy paper and rolls of tape from the teleprinter.
Panting, she ran past and up the stairs to the second.

The sounds of pursuit were loud behind her now. The barrel-chested doorman was only half a flight of stairs to her rear, and on the lower staircase the clatter of the bruised machine-shop men giving chase echoed between the dusty walls. Members of The Brotherhood on the editorial floor trooped out to see what the noise was all about—and over it all, the voice of Hilde could be heard rasping directions.

Emma ran into the printshop on the second floor. Work had been finished here; the stone was empty, the linotype machines untenanted, the lights—with the exception of one low-power bulb over the door—extinguished. She raced down the shadowy space between two rows of lino machines with barrel-chest and two others in close pursuit. Half way along, a hand press similar to the one on which she had been bound jutted a little way out into the passageway. She seized the wheel and twirled it violently as she passed. The steel platen slid smoothly out and blocked more of the gangway.

From behind came the confused sound of oaths and men cannoning into one another as barrel-chest sprawled headlong over the platen. Emma rounded the corner at the end of the gangway—and came abruptly to a halt.

George was standing there with a rubber truncheon in his hand.

The girl thought with frenzied speed. The last linotype machine in the row had been recently used: it was still switched on and humming quietly behind the keyboard, in among the spidery arms and selectors. At one side hung the domed reservoir with its electric immersion heater, three-quarters full of molten lead which the machine used to cast lines compiled by the operator at the keyboard. She advanced slowly. George raised the truncheon. He was grinning faintly.

Emma moved fast. She kicked out with her right foot, the tip of her boot darting out like a snake striking and hitting against the rim of the reservoir. The heavy metal cup canted sluggishly on its pivots, splashing molten lead in silvery gouts over George's arm and hand.

The rat-faced little man gave an animal howl and dropped to the floor, writhing.

Emma turned to meet the attack from behind. Barrel-chest and his two colleagues, having sorted themselves out from the press, were advancing at a run. The doorman came first. She seized his outstretched arm, bent forward and to one side, and hurled him over her shoulder in a simple hip throw.

Advancing to meet the other two, she held her right hand across her chest—palm downwards, fingers together, elbow up. There was a sudden flurry of activity. The girl kicked one man accurately on the kneecap, swung the edge of her right hand, held stiff and hard in the *karate* manner, in a vicious chop at the throat of the other . . . and then she was past, running back up the gangway between the machines.

More people were crowding in through the door from the landing. She turned at right angles, gasping for breath, and ran into the shop where the stones were. Surely she remembered a glass-paned door leading to a fire escape? Yes—there it was at the far end!

A big man with a beard was coming at her from the side. She took a running dive at the stone, evading his grasp by inches and skimming face-downwards along the length of the empty counter with hands and feet spread wide. The smooth jersey of her suit, unbroken by buttons or pockets, slid easily on the polished steel and she flew off at the far end with quite a turn of speed, keeping her feet with an effort and rushing across the short stretch of floor towards the fire escape.

She would have made it, if it hadn't been for a knot-hole in a floorboard. But the heel of one boot plunged into this aperture and jammed fast, pulling her up short and almost breaking her ankle. She struggled madly to get her foot out of the boot, but it reached almost to the knee and she hadn't manoeuvred her heel past the narrow section at the ankle before they were upon her.

Five minutes later she was lying on her back, bound hand and foot again, on a table in the editorial offices below. Her ankles and her knees were strapped together; her elbows and wrists were lashed together behind her back, and her arms were then roped to her body. The machine minders and compositors and operators stood, with the other Brotherhood men in the building, in a circle around the table. There seemed to be about fifteen of them in all. Only barrel-chest, who had returned to his post at the door, and George—whose whimpering cries could be heard from another room—were absent. Hilde stood behind Emma's head.

"Now—while we wait for the vans," she said, "I shall give

you a short demonstration. It can be a practical in our series on how to deal with the Opposition. I want to speak about keeping people quiet.

"A lot of nonsense is talked about gagging. There are only three ways of rendering a person *totally* soundless—by killing them, by making them unconscious, or by frightening them so much that they deliberately *refrain* from uttering a sound for fear of the consequences. Holding a gun on someone is a crude example of this.

"Failing these three, it is *impossible* to prevent a conscious person from uttering any sound whatever. The best we can do is to reduce that sound as far as is practical. Thus the gag.

"But as I say, much rubbish is talked about this. In films or television shows, for example, you see characters apparently speechless, unable to make any noise at all, just because they have a strip of some material tied over their mouths. In fact you could almost shout as loud with that as without.

"Two other kinds of gag are often used: plaster stuck *over* the mouth, or a strip of something tied *into* the mouth, dragging the corners back. These techniques inhibit the *articulation*; they stop the victim making words. But they cannot stop her making sounds. The vocal chords are unimpaired. Similarly with some object jammed into the mouth and tied in place with another—according to the position into which the mouth is forced, the various vowel sounds can all be uttered. If the mouth is held open, the sound *Ah* can be produced; if the lips are drawn back, the noise *Eee* will be made. Even if the lips are forcibly closed and the mouth filled, it will be possible to say *Mmmmm*—a kind of humming that can be quite loud.

"What we have to do therefore is to reduce the *resonance* of these noises as much as possible, so that they do not carry. You can forget about all the clever gags you ever heard of: plain cotton wool, more and more of it jammed into an open mouth, forced in everywhere, between the teeth and the cheek, under the tongue, between the lips and gums—this muffles the noise better than anything."

Hilde paused and looked down at the girl.

Emma's clear eyes gazed fearlessly round the circle of attentive faces—oafish, brutal, grasping, lustful, or just weak—as she wondered what kind of people they must be, who would join an organisation like this. And it wasn't even as if they were society's rejects: all these men must be highly skilled craftsmen, to be able to produce the four pages of a paper required, to Fleet Street standards.

The big woman was talking again. "Now in the case of this young woman here," she said, "the orders are that she is to be bound and gagged, wrapped round with a tarpaulin which is to be wired into place, taken aboard one of the aircraft and jettisoned over the North Sea with suitable weights attached to the —er—package. And the gagging must be good, as we shall have to carry out the package to the plane along with the bundles of newspapers, and there may be people around.

"Unfortunately, we have no cotton wool here. But we do have a large sponge. Which brings me to how you get a gag *in* the mouth of somebody determined to reject it. For this, you need two people . . . Alan, you can help.

"First, move the person so that the head hangs down over the end of a table. Geoff, Harry—just shift her up a bit, would you? . . . There! *That's* better. Thank you . . . Now, the mouth must be forcibly opened and held open. Hook the first two fingers of the right hand into the nostrils and bend the head back and down—so. Now—Alan! —the other person inserts his two forefingers in the two corners of the mouth, sliding them along inside the cheeks if necessary, and drags the lower jaw down— *so*. Then it is a simple matter to push in your sponge . . . slowly . . . bit by bit . . . like *that*!

"All you need now is a roll of insulating tape. Hold the hair out of the way . . . Thank you, Alan . . . and wind it round and round and round. The criss-cross of plaster is useless. By flexing the facial muscles, it can often be unstuck. The adhesive must be wound all round and stuck to *itself*.

"And now, you see the finished result—neat, economical, and practical, I think. If we administer a sharp pinch . . . *here*, for example—You see! The cry *can* be heard, but it's really quite muffled . . ."

Footsteps pounded on the stairs. The barrel-chested custodian of the doors burst into the room.

"The vans have arrived," he cried. "They're already in the yard. We've got to get downstairs and fold on the new pages in less than half an hour . . ."

17

"YOU CAN READ ALL ABOUT IT IN THE MORNING!"

THE helicopter edged down from the sky in the far corner of the airfield. The floodlights in its nose and tail cast twin pools of illumination on the concrete by the row of twin-engined private planes. It bounced twice in slow motion and then settled on its springs like an outsize cricket as the clatter of the rotors dwindled into silence.

Sandra Gillan jumped down from the perspex blister in the nose of the small aircraft and strode across the perimeter track towards the six private planes. A man in white overalls with the word *Courier* emblazoned across the front in facsimile of the paper's title block ran to meet her.

"The works passed on your message, Miss Gillan," he said. "The crates are ready to go any time you say. They're all warmed up and we've got clearance for the half-hour advance." He gestured towards the row of lighted windows charting the line of the airport buildings on the far side of the field. The lights of the control-tower operations room shone pale green above them.

"Good. The shipment should be here at any moment," Sandra Gillan said. "You didn't have any trouble with the other pilots —the two who aren't Brotherhood members?"

"Not on your life. They've had no idea that any of the stuff they've flown in has had anything to do with the fuss in the papers. So they saw no reason to query this flight. I just said the continental distributors had specially requested this edition early—and they swallowed it like lambs."

One of the other pilots came up to them. "Good evening, Miss Gillan," he said respectfully. "I'm on the northern run tonight. Do you want me to do Oslo and the other Scandinavian countries first—or make the circuit the other way round? I think the first way'd be better: the half-hour advance might make quite a difference at Brussels just now. They get very busy

176

about this time."

"I'm sure I don't know," Sandra Gillan said coldly. "Ask Mr Creighton: he's just coming now."

Robin Creighton had come down from the helicopter and was walking across the concrete towards them. With a word of apology, the pilot ran across and had a few words with him before returning to his plane.

Sandra Gillan looked after him with a frown. A breeze sprang up and whispered across the airfield, tolling the golden bell of her hair and plastering the white blouse to her figure. "I don't like that man, Robin," she complained as Creighton approached.

"Who? Green? Oh, he's all right, darling. Bit over-zealous, perhaps—but he's a good man. First-class pilot, too."

"He's obsequious. He makes my flesh creep. I think he's a Jewboy, Robin. You must get rid of him. Sack him at once."

Creighton patted her on the shoulder. "I'm more concerned at the moment with what happens to *us*," he said in his lardy voice.

"Us? Why nothing happens. We continue according to plan."

"You're quite sure this fellow Steed can't get here? After what happened to Morgan and the others at Silverstone this afternoon, I wouldn't put anything past him, you know."

"Morgan was a fool—trying to mix with someone on their own ground. Messing about in cars and boats is all that the decadent class Steed represents are any good at. It was the one field in which Steed was likely to worst him. He should have shot them both down when he saw them leave the *Clarion*."

"You may be right, my dear. But you haven't answered my question. Are you quite sure he can't get here?"

"How could he? I slugged him hard. He wouldn't have woken up until some time after we left. I'd have killed him, only I didn't know who might have known he'd been in our office prying about. But there are no trains at this time, it takes at least two hours to get here by car—even on Sunday—and there's no scheduled flight from London. The papers will have been distributed all over Europe long before he could make it. And all we have to do then is sit back and wait."

"You don't think we should—er—take a short continental holiday, just in case?"

"Of course not, Robin. What could Steed—or anyone—do

after the papers have gone? It'll bring the government down, there'll be an election—and The Brotherhood can move in. Once we've got a little power, we can make much more . . . No, the only danger was if Steed could have prevented the papers from being printed. Or prevented them from leaving."

A freight plane trundled along the runway and staggered into the air, its identification and signal lights flashing red, white and blue-green. Robin Creighton sighed. "Well, I hope you're right, Sandra darling, that's all," he said. "For anything to go wrong now, after twenty years, would be more than I could bear . . ."

"Of course I'm right. Nothing will go wrong. In a couple of months you'll be in Westminster, drumming up popularity for the party by screaming for the abolition of immigration, the registration of Jews, and so on. Don't *worry,* darling," She stood on tiptoe and kissed the full, moist lips.

Headlights blazed a path across the grassy outfield of the aerodrome. The low-set lamps raked along the line of parked aircraft and made mountains out of the ridges in the concrete, piling up shadow behind them and turning the group of pilots into long-legged giants. The vans were arriving from the *Clarion* . . .

There were three of them—two small ones of the kind used to deliver London evening newspapers to their sellers, and one larger, articulated truck with a covered top. From the interiors poured the fifteen men who had been printing the bogus front pages at Hanningford, the three two-man crews who had prepared the genuine editions for the substitution on the way from London, and the woman Hilde—now wearing her black raincoat again and carrying a small valise. The drivers remained behind their wheels.

The loading of the planes was obviously a rehearsed routine. Each man had a specific job to do; each bundle of papers with the inflammatory front page story quoting the Prime Minister had its appointed place in a particular aircraft. In ten minutes the last bundle had been stowed away.

Three of the men then staggered from the articulated van carrying between them a long tarpaulin package which appeared to be heavy—and with which they appeared to be having some difficulty. It was about the size of a roll of lino, and it was stoutly wired on the outside. Under the direction of

Hilde, the package was fed in through the rear door of the plane piloted by the man who had met Sandra Gillan when she came from the helicopter. They pushed it down as far as it would go into the tail. After they had returned to the van, Hilde leaned in and loosened the end of the tarpaulin next to her.

"I'm leaving this undone, my lovely," she crooned into the open end, "because once we take off, I shall remove your gag and we can talk. There's a nice suitcase full of lead type that we shall tie to your feet so that you sink well down—and I have a camera and flash bulb in this valise. I want to take your picture—just a close-up of the face—at the very moment that the door is opened and we slide you out over the sea."

Out on the apron, Creighton was talking to The Brotherhood men in a little group out of earshot of the pilots who were not members. "You have all done very well," he said quietly. "Once the planes have taken off, remember, we go to ground until we see what happens. Nobody is to meet any other member or be seen in his or her company until contacted by his local cell chief . . . Hilde will be going to Amsterdam with James—I think she must have a favourite club there!—and she will dispose of one—er—busybody on the way. Miss Gillan and I will be returning to London, where we temporarily incapacitated another this evening. I think we may have to make this permanent when we get back. Perhaps George—Where *is* George? Has anybody here seen George Harris?"

"He got burned a little," Hilde said. "I'm afraid we had to dispose of him. He couldn't keep quiet about it, and it was awkward . . ."

"Oh, what a pity. Never mind. We'll attend to it ourselves, then. But now—*on with the programme!*" He waved his arm. The men broke away and headed for the vans. One by one, the motors on the twin-engined aircraft coughed, whined and broke into life. Hilde hurried across the tarmac towards the leading plane. Creighton and Sandra turned towards the helicopter.

And suddenly a whistle shrilled piercingly three times.

A searchlight dazzled on from just beyond the row of planes, bathing everything in incandescent brilliance. And a voice, boxy and disembodied through an electrified loud-hailer, warned:

"This is a police action. You are completely surrounded. I call on you to lay down any arms you have and assemble here

in front of the searchlights . . ."

Creighton screamed.

It was the animal cry of a man frustrated beyond endurance, a man who sees the fruit of many years' work destroyed in a single moment. He frothed at the mouth and sawed at the air with his arms. *"The planes!"* he yelled. "Get the planes off the ground whatever happens! Shoot them . . . shoot them down like dogs!"

The members of The Brotherhood scattered in the beam of the searchlight—like cardboard cut-outs jerking to life in a film cartoon, in the stark black-and-white of that terrible light. Some of them flung themselves to the ground, produced revolvers or automatics and began firing in the direction of the loud-hailers; others ran for the shelter of the vans; one or two stood stupefied, as though dazed by the glare. Creighton and Sandra dodged behind the tail of the nearest plane.

The pilots who were not members of The Brotherhood cut their engines and climbed to the ground looking puzzled. Three of the other four aircraft revved their motors and swung slowly towards the runway, their rudders flapping from side to side, their wings quivering in the slipstream.

Once more the whistle shrilled—a long and a short blast, twice repeated, this time. It seemed to come from the direction of the articulated van.

Three police cars from somewhere beyond the searchlight started their engines and roared across the apron in a wide curve to intercept the aircraft. The second and third were able to rocket round in front of the planes and squeal to a halt inches from the squat central nacelles, effectively blocking their progress as the propellers of the twin engines spun uselessly on either side. The leading aircraft, however, was too far ahead for the first car to be able to do this—and the driver courageously drove his vehicle straight at the tailplane as the machine was accelerating away towards the main runway.

There was a splintering crunch. The rudder and elevators of the aircraft crumpled to nothing, the bonnet of the car flew up as the radiator buckled and the front wheels collapsed. Plane and car together slewed sideways and ground to a halt in a tangle of twisted wreckage. The police driver was slumped unconscious over his steering wheel.

Police now materialised on all sides from the darkness and

closed in on the natural arena formed by the searchlight. A spirited gun battle was momentarily halted when one of the gang succeeded in penetrating the toughened glass of the searchlight with a lucky bullet. The dazzling beam dwindled to nothing, the face of the light faded to orange, then vanished. Creighton was beside himself. "Take cover you idiots," he screamed. "Don't shoot it out from the middle of a *field*! Remember what you've been taught. Take cover and pick them off!" He beat furiously at the fuselage of the aircraft sheltering him. "Why don't you fly?" he bayed up into the sky. "Why is yours the one plane that hasn't tried? Get it off the *ground* . . ."

He yanked open the twin-engined plane's front door. His chief pilot was cowering on the floor under the instrument panel, his face grey with fear. "Get in that seat!" Creighton yelled. "Fly this crate off the ground . . . these papers *must* be delivered!" He looked towards the tail of the aircraft. The freight door was still open; he could see in the diffuse light the looming shapes of newsprint bundles and the long tarpaulin package that had been loaded last of all. The pilot spoke at last, his teeth chattering: "I'm s-s-sorry, Mr Creighton. I c-c-c-can't. I just can't. I never bargained for anything like this when I joined. I'm not a fighting man. I just can't . . . *Please*, Mr Creighton . . ."

Creighton gave a snort of disgust and jumped down from the step. Sandra and Hilde were nowhere to be seen. A smaller spotlight had been rigged up now, and by its radiance he could see a number of the gang and one or two policemen lying dead or wounded on the ground. The remainder of The Brotherhood men were being rounded up by a cordon of police. One or two isolated hand-to-hand fights still raged outside the illuminated area though, and the sporadic shouts of the law officers calling one to another were punctuated by the thud of blows and the scuffling gasps of men locked in combat.

The *Courier*'s Managing Editor dashed across the spotlit circle and pelted down beside the big articulated van in an attempt to gain his own helicopter. An arm inside a blue pinstriped sleeve dropped languidly from the driver's window as he passed the cab and hooked him round the ankle with the handle of an umbrella. He plunged to the ground with a crash that shook all the breath from his heavy body.

Almost without touching the van or the ground, it seemed, Steed was beside him. Lean fingers, surprisingly steely in their grip held one arm behind the big man's back. "This is a judo hold," the quiet voice drawled. "I wouldn't move too much: it might hurt. But get up." Creighton rose wearily to his feet. "Steed, of course," he said. "I might have known . . ."

"Mr Creighton, I presume," Steed said from behind him. "Or should I say Crandell Robins?"

"Oh—so you know that too?"

"Of course. It was too easy. They always use the same initials. Only you reversed yours, that's all."

"But how did you *get* here?"

"You're not the only man in England with a helicopter, Creighton—your proprietor has one too. He keeps it on the *Courier* roof, you may recall. He brought me up. We landed in the vacant lot near the *Clarion*—the one you wanted to make into a parade ground for fascists. I imagine he's still looking over the old *Clarion* building and the plant there. I think he's going to buy it . . ."

"Yes, yes: but how did you get *here*?"

"The driver of your larger lorry fell temptation to a little— er—stratagem, shall we say? So I took his place. And when your gentlemen and ladies were all nicely committed, I blew my little whistle and my friends came in."

"Damn you. How did you get on to us in the first place?"

"The microphone on Borridale's terrace. It was put there to hear the conversation he had with me and nothing else. There can't have been many people he'd have told that he was going to see me. You were one of them—and then, when we came out of *your* office, your secretary had been brushing against an outside wall, her hair was mussed up, she'd obviously done something strenuous in a hurry . . . and the mike had gone."

"Very clever," Creighton sneered. "Anything else, Mr Holmes?"

"Just the affair of the sub," Steed said mildly.

"Lindale? Come now—you can't tie me in with *that*!"

"I think the police can. You overheard him calling me. You saw him with the copy of *Hemming's* supplement in his hand—"

"But you *can't* know that. I burned the—" Creighton stopped, suddenly aware of what he was saying.

"You didn't know when you snatched the book away from him that one page was still crumpled in his fist—the very page that was to tip us off to the *Clarion* works. But you knew that *he* knew, so you knocked him out after luring him down to the machine room—which was easy enough for you to do as Managing Editor. Then you engineered his death with some of your employees who were also members of The Brotherhood. You returned to your own office while I was asking for him on the stone. When Len Fowles told me he'd gone to the basement, I went for the lift I'd come up in—the left-hand one—but it had gone back up to the eighth floor, where your office is."

"Any more?" Creighton asked with a sigh of affected boredom.

"Yes. You wanted at all costs to stall us until after this consignment went tonight. If the Prime Minister was involved, it would bring down the government, you felt. After that, it didn't matter what we found out ... So you had my flat watched, and when we came looking for the examples of the fake front pages that could have tipped us off to the old-fashioned type spotted by Lindale, and thus to the *Clarion*—you burned them and then tried to murder us with the help of your girl friend. When you failed, you ordered some of The Brotherhood to run us down in a car."

"Dear me, Mr Steed," Creighton said sarcastically, "I do seem to have been a naughty boy, don't I?"

"You've got a fair score there—murder, attempted murder, forgery, libel, I suppose, if Carew wanted to sue, conspiracy—and even treason, I should think. It should keep you busy for *another* twenty years!"

Most of the shouting and the shooting around them seemed to have died down. A superintendent of police approached, followed by two beefy flying squad men escorting a handcuffed Hilde.

"We've got the most of them rounded up now, Mr Steed," the superintendent said. "This—er—lady was one of the last."

"Oh, the cloakroom lady from the Cattery," Steed said with a smile. "I think I'll hang on to this umbrella. It's already tripped up your leader and your lot have ruined *one* for me this week..."

"We've checked the bundles of papers against the invoices," the policeman went on, "and we've accounted for all except one —*Look out! Stop her!*

Sandra Gillan was silhouetted against the spotlight, running awkwardly, almost waddling, with the missing bundle of papers clasped to her chest, towards the helicopter.

With a sudden galvanic move, Creighton broke free from Steed's hold and hared after her, running like the wind across the apron, bent low in case he was shot at. Steed made no attempt to follow him.

The superintendent was shouting orders, but none of his men were near enough to the helicopter to do much. Sandra Gillan was inside the machine now and Creighton was almost at the steps leading to the cabin door. The engine roared to life. A moment later, the whistling clatter of the rotors started up, and the machine rose slowly into the air.

"Let them go," Steed said nonchalantly to the furious policeman. "Let them go; it'll do no harm."

"But surely one bundle of several dozen newspapers, properly distributed, could do as much damage as hundreds—if the forgeries are the dynamite you said they were?"

"It could if they were," Steed said with a smile. "But I'm very much afraid they won't be."

"What d'you mean, Mr Steed?"

"If she's using the flight instructions prepared for the *Courier* planes—and I'm sure she must be; she probably nicked one from one of the cockpits while we were all talking—she's going to find there's a mistake been made about the flight path. And they're trying out the new multiple-barrel anti-aircraft rocket batteries over the Channel tonight . . . Somehow, I feel there may be a most unfortunate accident—especially if any unscheduled, unidentified aircraft stray into the zone . . ."

A confused mumbling noise manifested itself as the whining drone of the helicopter died away towards the east.

"Mrs *Peel*!" Steel exclaimed in dismay. "I'm most frightfully sorry: I completely forgot. *Do* forgive me . . ."

He hauled the tarpaulin package from the tail of the nearest plane and began unwiring the fastenings with his own hands. Soon he had freed enough of the wire to turn down the heavy material sufficiently to reveal Emma's head and shoulders. As he began to strip off the insulating tape retaining the sponge in her mouth, the outraged gargling sounds continued unabated.

"You see what I mean?" the handcuffed Hilde said to nobody in particular. "That's what I said: you simply *can't* shut them up. They can always make *some* noise . . ."

"My dear, I really do feel it was *most* remiss of me . . ." Steed began when he had unwound the last of the tape and tweaked out the sponge. But Emma interrupted before he could finish:

"Never mind about all that! What's *happened*? Tell me what's happened! How did you *get* here? What was all that shooting? Did you manage to stop the bogus papers from going? Did we capture the gang? . . ."

Steed eased the long length of the girl from the tube-like package of tarpaulin. He rolled her over on to her face and unbuckled the straps around her elbows and wrists.

"Such a lot's happened," he said as he worked away, "that I wouldn't know where to start. But the *Courier* will definitely be having a no-star tomorrow morning—you can read all about it in the papers . . ."

18

A MAN WITHOUT A ROSEBUD

"I DON'T know what His Nibs is thinking of," Benson said as he reached behind him to open the taxi door for Steed in Jermyn Street. "Putting the cab at your disposal the whole day long while your old wreck gets all the bullet holes taken out of it! Fired them yourself, I shouldn't wonder, to save the petrol. It must use a fair torrent."

"It's not the cheapest car to run," Steed admitted.

"And I suppose I've got to tool about here all morning, trying to avoid getting knocked off by the law for illegal parking, while you sit in front of a ruddy great glass, smirking," Benson grumbled.

"I have a luncheon engagement with Mrs Peel at Prunier's, Benson."

"That's different. See you in two hours then, cock." He closed the door, wound the luggage strap round the *For Hire* flag and drove away with a grin.

The atmosphere in Jeffrey's was cool, moist and scented— an agreeable change from the thundery heat outside.

"I never heard of anything so ridiculous in my life," General Anstruther was saying. "Don't you think it's ridiculous, Jeffrey? Don't you think it's one of the dammedest things you ever heard of, eh?"

Jeffrey switched off the drier, reached into his breast pocket for a comb and nodded. "It's certainly an unusual idea, General," he said.

"No, but I mean, honestly—sending a team of six mannequins to the top of the Matterhorn, with a photographer, just to prove that the modern young woman is as fit and adventurous as her mother was . . . why it's—it's not right. It's a newspaper stunt of the worst kind."

What there was of Sir Charles's hair was being backwashed. "Oh, I don't know, old boy," he said out of the shampoo suds.

"I suppose they get fed up with everybody saying that they're either hermaphrodites like the Olympic competitors or brainless asses like the debs . . . I *say*, Robin! That *is* a bit warm, you know."

The fat man was suffering a friction, his empurpled head bobbing slowly up and down as the hairdresser's hands ravaged his scalp. "So far as the *papers* go," he said between strokes, "I suppose you can't . . . blame them for trying . . . to get something different . . . as often as possible. But some of the stunts like this . . . well, you'd think they . . . might just as well *invent* the bloody stories . . ."

"I don't care what you fellers say," General Anstruther went on, "I think it's not decent, really I—Why, hallo! Here's young Steed! Haven't seen you for several days, Steed. What's been happening to you?"

"Good morning, General. No—I took a job for a few days," Steed said deprecatingly, handing his hat and stick to Adrian and beckoning to the manicurist. "I was working on a newspaper."

"Oh. Writin'. Not much in my line, though I daresay it's agreeable enough for those with a taste for it," the General said. "I'm sure you could do better than some of the chaps we were speaking of when you came in!"

Adrian helped Steed off with his jacket and brought a hanger. "But, Mr Steed!" he said, dismayed. "You're not wearing a rosebud today!"

"Good Lord, so I'm not," Steed said blankly. "Must have been working harder than I thought. I didn't have time to go down to the old place over the weekend and get some of our own, so I suppose I sort of forgot. Never mind—we'll put it right later in the week."

"But Mr Steed—I have the claret glass all ready on your shelf."

"Then it shall not be disappointed, Adrian. Glasses, as you rightly imply, are meant to be used. Hand me my umbrella, if you please."

"Your umbrella, Mr Steed? You're not leaving?"

"My umbrella. No, indeed I am not."

The hairdresser handed the umbrella across. Steed took hold of the handle, unscrewed it, and laid it down on the marble basin. "This one has a hollow shaft," he said, removing a tiny cork and reaching for the claret glass. "It takes a half bottle, you know! At the moment I'm carrying a very ordinary St Emilion—just to see how it travels before I order any from France."

He poured carefully and held the glass critically up to the light.

"Not bad, not bad," he said. "But any umbrella that has already put a would-be dictator to flight is hardly likely to be vanquished by a simple wine glass . . ."

COLUMBO
THE GRASSY KNOLL

by William Harrington

Lt Columbo, everyone's favourite rumpled TV detective, must unravel the mystery that has held the world's attention for thirty years: who killed JFK?

Controversial talk-show host Paul Drury is silent - murdered in his hillside mansion. Discounting burglary as a motive, Columbo soon finds out how many people had reason to kill the arrogant celebrity: Alice Drury, his beautiful ex-wife; Bobby Angele, top country singer; Jessica O'Neill, famous movie star.

But Columbo's next discovery is more startling still. Someone sabotaged the broadcast of Drury's final show, which promised to expose JFK's real assassin. Now, the computer files of that show are gone - perhaps destroyed by the killer of Paul Drury?

Before Columbo solves the mystery, he has to deal with another: Thirty years ago in Dallas, who shot JFK?

This all-new mystery is the first in a series of original Columbo novels from Titan Books.